Serena Gray is the a [...]
Beached on the Shores [...] *and*
then You Diet. Her work has appeared in *Cosmopolitan*
and *Woman's Own.*

Also by Serena Gray

THE SLAG'S ALMANAC
BEACHED ON THE SHORES OF LOVE
LIFE'S A BITCH ... AND THEN YOU DIET

THE ALIEN'S SURVIVAL MANUAL
AN OUTSIDER'S GUIDE TO THE PLANET EARTH

Serena Gray

Futura

A Futura Book

First published in Great Britain in 1992 by Futura Publications
A Division of Macdonald & Co (Publishers) Ltd
London & Sydney

ISBN 0 7088 5326 9

Typeset by Leaper & Gard Limited, Great Britain
Printed in Great Britain by Cox & Wyman Ltd,
Reading, Berks.

Futura Publications
A Division of
Macdonald & Co (Publishers) Ltd
165 Great Dover Street
London SE1 4YA

A member of Maxwell Macmillan Publishing Corporation

Dedication

This book is dedicated to any creature — of any time and any species — who has ever found him or herself on the Earth, gazing up at the sky at three in the morning, and wondering how to get off.

'Anywhere you wander,
Anywhere you berth,
Anywhere you find yourself,
There's no place like Earth.'

Old tellurian song

'Bet you don't have anything like this where you come from'

Old tellurian saying

'Uh oh'

Normal reaction of the first-time visitor

Contents

Editor's Note

Although the Earth is small when you compare it to the rest of the universe, it is also large. That is, it contains many diverse nations and peoples. But although these many diverse nations and peoples have lived together for thousands and thousands of years, none of them seems to either understand or like each other very much. Quite the contrary, in fact. That is why, although all humans have similar biological, physical and emotional needs, to listen to them and watch them carry on, you would think that they were the ones who came from different planets.

For the purposes of this work, however, it would have been impossible — as well as unnecessary and, in the final analysis, futile — to detail every separate human society. Therefore, we have taken as our rough model the Western World.

There are three reasons for this:

1. The Western World is dominant.
2. The Western World is up to its neck in the twentieth century, and thus represents state-of-the-art Man.
3. The television is better in the West and there's generally less open warfare on the streets (except, perhaps, in Ireland and Brooklyn).

Introduction

*'The most incomprehensible thing about the world is that
it is comprehensible'*
Albert Einstein[1]

The most striking difference between the Earth and other,
more readily accessible planets lies not in its physical
structure or make-up. So what if it only has one sun and
one moon? So what if its sky is predominantly blue? What
importance is there in the fact that both the three-toed
sloth and the brussel sprout call it home? Even tellurians
themselves don't seem to care about its atmosphere or its
other inhabitants. No, the most striking difference
between the Earth and any other planet in the cosmos is
Man.

Man did not always exist.[2] Because of this, the planet
Earth — like pizza, the plastic bag and politics — at first
seemed like a pretty good idea.

There it was, a small but not unattractive oblate
spheroid, close enough to its sun to make it possible to
grow alfalfa and to surf all year, but not so close that one
would melt. This proximity to a friendly heat source,
combined with what was once a benign atmosphere, not
only made it seem unlikely that one might have to learn to

---

[1] Outsiders have long wondered precisely what Dr Einstein
meant by this. That is: by whom?

[2] It is as difficult for Man himself to appreciate this point as it
is for him to appreciate the further point that he will not
always.

breathe through one's tail (as has happened elsewhere), but also meant that the Earth was capable of supporting a variety of life-forms in a generally comfortable and even pleasant way.

Indeed, looking through those early photographs, one can imagine precisely how pleased the Earth's creator must have been. Forget Tikata Major with its waist-deep orange clouds and one type of shrub. Forget Outer Lipisky with its querulous monsters and silver sand. Stop trying to come to terms with that chain of planets in the Oatian Galaxy where everybody hops and sucks nitrogen. What potential the Earth had! What promise! What astounding possibilities! What good ideas oxygen and rainfall were!

And so the thought occurred: Where couldn't this planet go from here?

The question was almost immediately answered by the very being who had asked it. Anywhere. Instinctively recognizing the limitations of the single cell, the creator went on to bigger and better things. Pond scum. Cockroaches. Reptiles. Bats.

And then, spurred on by this early success, the Earth's creator began shifting around icebergs, breaking up continents, and experimenting wildly with the flora and fauna.

'I'm on to something good here,' the Earth's creator gloated.

Mad with inspiration, the creator then scratched the dinosaur, and started fooling around with newer, more streamlined concepts.

Smugness set in. And why not? Those blue skies and clear green oceans. Those snow-capped purple mountains and heartbreaking sunsets. Those luscious jungles and valleys. Those lazy deserts and forest streams. The Hebrides. The Grand Canyon. Africa. Southeast Asia. The aurora borealis. Carpets of bluebells. Clouds of butterflies. Phantasmagoric gatherings of mineral, animal and vegetable. The golden hawk and the fin-back whale.

The last-minute thought.

Anyone who had made all that would have happily taken a pat on the back.

But the Earth's creator, as it transpired, didn't quite know when to stop. For just when the future was looking exceptionally bright — and a good fourteen years after a rest might have been indicated — along came Man.

'Never mind Outer Wampumata and the Spaxic Solar System!' the Earth's creator shouted. 'This is it! At last, a planet that can maintain a species that looks good in three-piece suits and can put out a fire.'

Unjustified optimism, of course. But, then, who was to know?

The simple truth, however, is that until Man started ascending, the Earth was no more difficult to figure out than any other planet in the universe. Tricky during droughts, ice ages and the more apocalyptic sort of storm, perhaps, but not impossible. In those good old, pre-*Homo sapien* days, there was a certain symmetry and equilibrium to the planet. Once you'd mastered the finer points of nourishment, body maintenance, reproduction and self-protection (e.g. don't eat anything that might bite back, don't shit in your own water supply, stay away from close relatives, and show a lot of teeth or antennae), you were pretty well set. Things worked.

But not any longer.

Since Man's much-publicized ascent,[3] this single species has come to dominate the entire globe. No more peaceful co-existence. No more interspecies give and take. No more balance. Precious little natural selection. Ever since that fateful swing from the trees, everything on Earth has been determined by what Man wants or thinks he wants, when he wants it, and how he plans to get it.

These days, any visitor to the planet must grapple with a complicated, often hazardous and always dumbfounding cultural, societal and emotional structure that is commonly known as Twentieth-Century Life. Twentieth-Century Life is completely the responsibility of Man. The rest of the planet would have been perfectly happy left to its own devices in the year 1,000,002 BC.

Contemporary human existence is so difficult to understand (even for most humans) that tourism has dropped off significantly in the last two or three centuries. Many the nervous alien who has turned around just outside the Earth's atmosphere, choosing to visit some galactic backwater where the only entertainment is the occasional imploding star, rather than risk getting lost in Disneyland or Liverpool.

---

[3] This ascent, one might note, has been publicized by no one but Man. Extraterrestrial anthropologists, sociologists and historians have always been much more interested in cetaceous mammals, and all other Earth inhabitants have been too occupied trying to live with it to applaud it.

The following excerpt from *Is It Worth the Trip? Recent Explorations of Tellus* is typical.

Artumo Seselked, from the planet Tu

I first visited the Earth in 1833. The moment I was beamed down in Little Garump, Dorset, I experienced a feeling of panic and powerlessness like none I had ever experienced before, not even all those eons I was lost in time. I think I was expecting something more like Tu, but without the yellow sky and mugwap canals. You can see how naïve I was. Although I had fifty billion years of Tu culture and experience behind me, I certainly couldn't be considered prepared. What were fifty billion years of reason and order compared to Little Garump? One minute I was dodging black holes, and the next I was standing in a large, dark room that smelled like an old fuselage, surrounded by a dozen or so men with large glasses in their hands. It was difficult to make out their faces clearly, because there was something burning in the room and it was filled with smoke, but they seemed to be smiling and laughing. I took this to mean that they were happy, and, further, that they were pleased to see me. They beat me up, stole my boots, and tied me to the back of a cow. The cow and I wandered through the countryside for several days before my shipmates rescued me. The only thing of note I discovered was that I'd been wrong about the canals.

And so here, after centuries of head-slapping, worry, speculation, myth, propaganda, and abject terror, is real help and useful advice. Exhaustively researched, personally tested, and unconditionally guaranteed.

Part One — The Overview

'Welcome to the Planet Earth.
You'll get used to it in time.'

Chapter One

So You Want to See the Planet Earth
'Not only is this not Kansas,
it's not the planet Ackba either'

Why the Earth?

Basically, there is no real answer to that question. It's there, of course, which is one reason. And it may not be there for much longer, which gives it a certain anthropological interest. But other than that, the typical response is, 'Why not?'

Humans are obsessed with the idea that for billions of years no one in the universe has had anything better to do than to visit them. Whenever something happens that they don't understand, or they feel a little lonely and unsure, they decide that their planet must have been visited by aliens again.[4] They use this theory to explain everything from natural rock formations to the disappearance of the dinosaur.[5]

The fact of the matter is, however, that no one has ever had much desire to come here at all. If the seas weren't boiling or the whole thing covered with ice, then there was always some war or reign of terror going on that made

---

[4] Only man, of all the creatures who have ever existed in the cosmos, is capable of looking at a primitive cave drawing of two hunters and an elk and saying, 'Hey, I think the bloke on the left must be from another planet, see how pointed his ears are?'

travel difficult, not to mention inadvisable. Not even the most thrill-seeking Xuption, for example, was going to risk the fall of Rome, the Inquisition, or Hitler's Germany. There have always been thousands more attractive, stimulating and hospitable planets to go to.[6]

Nonetheless — due in no small part to the way Man has recently begun to thump around the solar system, sending out probes, blaring rock'n'roll music, and trying to turn his galaxy into a militarized zone — a certain curiosity has built up over the millennia. Who is Chuck Berry? Why was Marilyn so unhappy? What is a ziploc bag? Why would you want to put crackers in it? How can you explain the popularity of alcohol, dinner parties, subtitled films about incest or suicide, Jeffrey Archer, or Ronald Reagan? Why aren't the batteries ever included?

[5] There is a tellurian legend that the dinosaurs were colonists from another solar system, and that, suddenly tired of thudding through the swamps of Earth, they packed up their things and went back home. Thinking that everyone else in the universe is anxious to visit their planet is, however, a common human delusion, and there is no evidence to support this theory. Bulooga Bulooga, the eminent Zemon historian, has alternatively suggested that the dinosaurs, seeing the way the evolutionary ladder was progressing, decided to get out while the going was good, before the arrival of Man. 'Why risk being turned into a bag or a circus act if you can possibly avoid it?' reasons Bulooga.

[6] True enough, there was a brief period there, between the last glacial epoch and the invention of the wheel, when it wasn't a bad place to go if you had a liking for the primitive or wanted somewhere where there was no chance of running into anyone you knew (who would ever think to look for you in a peat bog, after all?), but, in general, it is fair to say that as the Earth began as an empty, broiling mass, and as Man has been doing his best to get it back to that state as quickly as he can, it has never been the universe's answer to the Côte d'Azur. A being from Atzitl would be as likely to choose the Earth as a good place to spend the winter, as a civil servant in London would be to choose Minsk.

What are the silver sands of Outer Lipisky compared to Earth?

A Brief History of the Planet Earth

Things started slowly. First there was nothing, just another piece of cosmic landscape with the usual quantum carryings on; and then there wasn't. Life began. It wasn't brought in someone's suitcase, it just happened. Though not too fast. It is Man, not Nature, who is always in a hurry. One cell here, and one cell there. Then two cells, etc. Then diversity took hold. Diversity and adaptation. One day pond scum, the next day the reptile. Things continued apace.

During its Golden Age (when those interested in getting away from it all might have considered Tellus), life there was balanced and harmonious. That is not to say there wasn't bloodshed. There was bloodshed. That is not to say that there weren't times of stress and argument. There were those times. All things have to eat, after all. Even plants can be territorial. But, on the whole, things rolled along in a peaceable way. Everything fitted together. A lot happened, but no one bothered to write

Man prides himself on being unique.

any of it down or sell it to the *Sun* for half a million. This period was known as prehistory.

And then along came Man. History began.

The story of most life-forms can be summed up in one word: survival.

Man, however, because of what he likes to think of as his superior intelligence, had survival pretty much sewn up from the start. He whizzed through the basics — shelter, heat, agriculture — while everyone else was still looking for somewhere to go in the rain and gnawing on bark.

He went straight from survival to power. From power, it was one small step to unbridled greed, and its close allies violence, corruption, treachery, hypocrisy and abject terror.

So much for history.

So That's It?

In a nutshell.

Chapter Two

Tourism Made Simple
'Be prepared'

Jiji Jinoma, from the planet Marzelpod

On my first trip to Earth, to make an initial
assessment of its contributions to cosmic culture,
I went to Rome, Italy, with some people from
Wisconsin whom I met in a Taco Bell in
Piccadilly Circus. They were homesick, and I was
homesick (they missed English muffins, a
delicacy not available in England, and a
television programme called 'Jeopardy', which
Mrs Muduska was better at than Mr Muduska;
and I missed the underpopulation of Marzelpod
and its crystallized sky), so it seemed natural that
we should team up. At least, it seemed natural in
a booth at Taco Bell when one was trying to
decide whether the object before one was to be
eaten or allowed to dry out and used as a
weapon.

Our first mistake was that we went by train.
The Muduskas insisted on travelling overland,
because, they said, they wanted 'to see the
country' (by which I took it they meant the
continent of Europe). Mrs Muduska spent the
entire journey alternating between telling me her
life story (which was oddly fascinating, because
so little seemed to happen in it outside of a

supermarket, kitchen or TV room) and reading a book that, she assured me, was just like the last sixteen books she'd read (she seemed to enjoy it). Mr Muduska slept and ate. As soon as he'd eaten, he'd go back to sleep, saying, 'Wake me when we get there,' and Mrs Muduska would laugh. None of us ever knew where we were. 'Where are we now?' Mrs Muduska would ask me periodically. I'd say I didn't know. Then she'd ask, 'Are we still in France?' I'd say I wasn't sure. 'Is this Spain?' she'd want to know. I'd say that it was hard to tell. Panic would overtake her. 'I didn't miss the Alps, did I?' she'd demand. At about that point, Mr Muduska usually woke up. 'Are we there yet?' he'd inquire. 'Is there anything left to eat?' It was a long trip.

Our second mistake was to go at all. The Muduskas hated Rome. 'It may have culture,' Mrs Muduska kept saying, 'but it's not as nice as Madison.' The streets were too narrow and the avenues too wide. Mrs Muduska said that while she hadn't expected the hotel to live up to the standards set by the Holiday Inn in Madison, the beds were much too soft and the shower wasn't hot enough. Nor were the Muduskas impressed with the Romans. The Romans were loud (whenever we stopped someone to ask for directions they would shout at us), unhelpful (when they shouted at us it was always in Italian), and rude (they tended to laugh or just stare blankly when the Muduskas shouted back in English). Mrs Muduska was not only sure that they were pretending not to understand English, she was sure they were overcharging us for everything as well. (This did not, however, stop her from buying several dozen spoons, thermometers, and plates decorated with either a wolf, a temple, or a gladiator and the word

Roma, and a lamp that looked like the Colosseum.) Mr Muduska and I soon grew weary of ruins, the two of us sharing the opinion that having seen one pile of old stones, you'd pretty much seen them all.[7] Mrs Muduska, insistent that we were missing out on an important cultural experience, moved us on to churches and museums, until Mr Muduska, weary of them as well, bought some slides of Rome, its art and its artifacts, and we retired to one of the restaurants recommended by a friend of Mrs Muduska whose daughter had spent two weeks in Rome the summer before.

It was then that Mr Muduska announced that he thought the Romans were trying to kill him.

'It's a plot,' said Mr Muduska. 'They hate Americans.'

Mrs Muduska wrinkled her nose. 'Does the water taste funny, or is it me?' she asked.

'It's because they're all Mafia,' continued Mr Muduska. 'They say they're not, but you can't fool me.' He winked. 'They're as thick as thieves.' He laughed, poked me in the ribs, and winked again. 'Well, they would be, wouldn't they?' he joked.

Mrs Muduska sniffed the butter. 'Do you think this butter comes from *cows*?' she wondered aloud.

I said I didn't think the Romans were purposely trying to run him over, that it was just

---

[7] JiJi is not the first to find the human fascination with their own debris a little tiresome. Many an extraterrestrial observer has found it difficult to fathom how the species that invented genocide (and the only one to ever use it) can become sentimental and emotional over old buildings — even to the point of inventing a bomb that destroys living things but leaves edifices intact.

the way they drove, which, as Mrs Muduska had already pointed out several times, wasn't anything like the way people drove in Wisconsin.

Although, of course, Mr Muduska wasn't speaking Italian, he lowered his voice. 'Then how do you explain the food?' he asked.

'The food?' The food in Rome was one of the few things I'd found on Earth that seemed like a real contribution to anything. The olives alone were worth a couple of Umbian dances and the Metax Field Theory.

'Yes,' he hissed, 'the food. You think I don't know when I'm bein' poisoned?'

Mrs Muduska leaned towards me. 'It's the garlic,' she said, patting his arm. 'Hank hates garlic. It's so foreign.'

'It's not just the garlic,' said Hank. 'There's all these other little things floatin' around.' He speared something small, round and greenish with his fork. 'What's this?' he demanded.

I was about to say that it looked a lot like a Caringian nerve pellet, when Mrs Muduska cut me off. 'I think it's a caper,' said Mrs Muduska.

I was curious. I wasn't familiar with the word in connection with spaghetti sauce. 'What's a caper?'

'I'm not sure,' Mrs Muduska admitted. 'I think it comes from the sea.'

'This is no fish,' said Mr Muduska. 'It looks like rabbit shit.'

'No, no,' soothed Mrs Muduska, 'I'm sure it's related to shrimp.'

But Mr Muduska would not be soothed. Worried that he might never make it back to Wisconsin, he refused to eat anything but bread, of which he ate three baskets. It took us nearly an hour to pay for our meal, because the Muduskas then spent forty-five minutes haggling with the

10

waitress over whether or not the bread was
included in the meal.

'You see what I mean?' said Mrs Muduska, as
we finally limped towards our hotel. 'They try to
squeeze every penny they can out of you.'

The Typical Tourist

As technological progress has made the globe smaller,
international and intercontinental travel have become
commonplace. A hundred years ago, most people would
be born, live and die in the same town or village. The
chances of Annie Smith from Wapping spending a week in
Greece or seven days and five nights in Torres Molinas
were no greater than the chances of you running into a
man-made satellite in the Martian orbit.

These days, however, few people ever seem to stay at
home. You can hardly stop to look at a church without

Humans travel to learn, experience and grow.

11

being trampled by twenty tourists with video cameras filming each other sitting on a headstone.

From the extraterrestrial point of view, there are two facts about human tourists that are worth remembering.

The first is that although everyone makes a lot of money out of tourists, no one ever seems to like them very much.[8]

The second is that while most extraterrestrials tend to follow the old maxim, 'When in Xzygo, do as the Xzygoans do', humans have no such compunctions. No matter where they go on their planet, they always behave as though they wished they'd stayed at home, and even when they do find something they approve of — a hillock, for example, or a particularly agreeable cucumber — it is always because it reminds them of something from home (although, of course, it will never quite live up to that item).[9]

You, of course, may not wish to bring attention to yourself by wearing Bermuda shorts and a baseball cap with a moosehead on it, but there are still several obvious advantages to knowing how tourists on Earth are expected to behave. Firstly, it will enable you to distinguish them from non-tourists. This is handy if you are in need of directions, information, or a post office.[10] It is also handy should someone with a gun approach you in the parking lot of a bar in Maryland one night to ask why you didn't stand during the National Anthem. You will then know enough to clap one hand around his shoulder and to say very loudly in broken English, 'Thank you for winning the war for us.'[11]

---

[8] This is not always as irrational as it seems. It is one thing hating someone who has come to your country to spend too much on hotel rooms and souvenirs so much that you triple-charge them for the cab ride from the airport. It is something else to feel a little disgruntled towards planeloads of men in perma-press suits carrying cam recorders who only come to your land to have sex with twelve-year-old girls.

12

Humans love taking quizzes, especially if they aren't actually *for* anything. They become panicky if tested on their knowledge of history or open-heart surgery, but ask them to fill out a questionnaire to determine whether or not they have a good sex life (something you would presume they would already know) and they're as happy as a hadron. So, to get you in the mood for Earth, here is a short quiz that will test your T.A. (Tourist Acumen).

For each question, simply select the answer you think most typical humans would choose.

⁹. Mariri U, from Ael, tells this anecdote:
'In 1969, some friends and I decided to spend the summer hiking through Great Britain. I'm not sure why any more, but it seemed like a good idea at the time. There were quite a lot of rumours about how exciting and interesting it was. No one had warned us about either the weather or the food. Anyway, we decided to visit Stonehenge. The landlady in the bed and breakfast told us that many people believed Stonehenge had been laid out by witches, but that she knew for a fact that it was an ancient landing strip used by alien aviators who colonized Britain during the time of the Druids. I asked her why any beings capable of intergalactic travel would want to colonize pre-Roman Britain and she said, "They needed the genes, didn't they?" So, anyway, we went to see this important monument. There were some big rocks, piled up on one another. We were standing there, looking at them (what else could you do?), when two American women came to stand in front of us. One of them turned to the other. "Don't it look just like Wisconsin?" she said. Her companion said, "Spitting image, it like to make me cry." Personally, It reminded me a lot more of the third moon of Galuup, but I didn't like to say anything.'
¹⁰ It is a known fact that on Earth, unlike on any other planet that has ever been, people will give you information, directions, or the location of the local post office, whether they know it or not. In fact, it has been observed on more than one occasion that the less a human knows about something, the more ready s/he will be to explain it in full.
¹¹ This, in fact, is an all-purpose phrase it would be good for you to know. It doesn't matter what war, there's always one that's applicable.

1. You are a male human from the North of England. You are going to Majorca for twelve days and ten nights. Into your over-sized neon-pink and purple bag you pack:

   a. ordinary, everyday, practical clothes that require no special laundering, little ironing, and that are acceptable wear for most occasions, including a swimsuit, a warm jumper, and a raincoat.

   b. several pairs of floral shorts in bright colours, T-shirts with slogans such as 'Life's a Bitch and Then You Die', 'All Male', and 'Someone in Milton Keynes Loves Me', three Hawaiian shirts, a pink sweatshirt with someone else's name across the chest, a small swimsuit and a plaid jacket.

   c. the test-for-blindness shorts, the T-shirts, the Hawaiian shirts, the sweatshirt, the swimsuit, a football scarf, several packets of Superman condoms, and seventy-two cans of your favourite lager.

2. You are a female human from the North of England. You are going to Majorca for twelve days and ten nights. Into your over-sized neon-pink and purple bag you pack:

   a. ordinary, everyday, practical clothes that require no special laundering, little ironing and that are acceptable wear for most occasions, including a swimsuit meant for swimming, a warm jumper, and a raincoat.

   b. several pairs of short shorts, twenty halter tops, ten without the halter, five bikinis, something iridescent that looks like a tube to wear to the disco and three sheath dresses that almost cover your thighs, one patterned like the skin of a leopard, one like the skin of a zebra, and one like the walls of an Indian restaurant.

c. the shorts, the tops, six bikini bottoms, the something iridescent, the sheaths, a pair of hot-pink toreador pants, six pairs of high heels, a hairdryer, a hair crimper, several boxes of waxing strips and a chest expander.

3. On the plane *en route* to Majorca you:

   a. don't eat or drink anything, because you have read that your body adjusts better if you don't, and, anyway, having spent sixteen hours in the air terminal, waiting for your flight, you're pretty tired of eating and drinking.

   b. get pissed as a newt.[12]

   c. get pissed as a newt, lead the entire plane in several choruses of 'Surfing Safari', and then pass out in the loo.

4. During your twelve days and ten nights in Majorca you:

   a. enjoy going off on your own every day to see the local sights, meet people, and absorb the customs and atmosphere of this place that is so different to your home.

   b. never leave the hotel.

[12] Extensive research has failed to reveal any clue as to what this expression could possibly mean. That is to say, we know what it means — that the person in question has imbibed so much alcohol that their nervous system is in a state of temporary paralysis — but we don't know what it could possibly have to do with newts. There is only one creature on the planet that intoxicates itself to the point where it falls asleep with its face in its dinner, and it certainly isn't the newt.

c. never leave the hotel, though you couldn't even if you wanted to (not that you do), because you got such a bad sunburn your first day on the beach that you spend five of your twelve days lying on your stomach, complaining because all the television shows are in a foreign language, and the other seven sitting on the loo, because you didn't believe the warnings about the water.

5. You are a human from a part of the world that is known for its food in much the same way that Turkey is known for its prisons. For your holiday of a lifetime, you go to a country whose cuisine can only be talked about realistically in epic verse. Even eating a sandwich in this country is an experience worth a haiku or two. You:

   a. literally have the time of your life. You are like a creature raised in a cellar suddenly introduced to sunset over the Grand Canyon. You can't believe all this incredible food existed while you were eating tinned beans, chips and mushy peas. You try everything.

   b. you try one thing, but you don't like it much.

   c. you find the McDonald's as soon as you unpack, though, as you mention on every postcard you send home, the hamburgers just don't taste the same.

6. You have travelled twelve thousand miles to visit Paradise. Paradise is a remarkable land of excitement, beauty, pageantry and history. You:

   a. don't send one postcard home the entire time you're there, you're so busy exploring this strange and endlessly fascinating place.

b. send thirty-six postcards home. They are all the kind that have a cartoon on the front and a checklist describing your holiday, which you dutifully check off as it saves having to write individual messages. These postcards were designed in England and printed in China.

c. only leave the hotel to go to McDonald's three times a day, you're so busy writing postcards. Your favourite is solid black with the slogan 'Paradise at Night' across it.

7. Afterwards, the thing you remember most about Paradise — and the thing you are still talking about years later — is:

a. sitting on the silvery sand in the moonlight while the palm trees sway, and out on the ocean the flickering lanterns of tiny fishing boats shine like stars.

b. the toilets — they were holes in the ground.

c. the fact that no one there had ever heard of Cadbury's chocolate.

8. When dealing with someone who doesn't speak your language the best way to communicate is to:

a. try and learn a few key phrases that will enable you to communicate basic thoughts and actions (cold, hot, far, late, food, etc.), and keep a dictionary handy.

b. shout.

c. shout, but in a broken version of your language that the person couldn't possibly understand even if s/he were fluent in it.

9. Imagine that you are travelling by jeep through a poor but exotic country. You are fascinated by the scenery and by the glimpses you get of native life. High in the mountains, you come to a remote and isolated village, where few foreigners have ever been and most of the children are dressed in clothes from the Christian Mission. Your first instinct is to:

a. drive on, there is no place for you here.

b. take a picture.

c. get someone to take your picture with a few chickens and children around you.

Give yourself one (1) point for every a.; two (2) for every b.; and three (3) for every c.

If you scored a total of nine points, you don't know much about human tourists. Between nine and thirteen, you're still looking at the world through the wrong end of the stectrascope. Eighteen, you have a solid grasp of human behaviour. Eighteen to twenty-two, you may have been spending a little more time than is necessary in souvenir shops. Twenty-seven, it's possible that you may know more than is really good for you.

The Global Village

As ideas go, this is a fairly recent one for Western Man. As explained by several popular newspapers and magazines, what it means is that Man no longer sees the globe as divided into separate, distinct — and largely warring — nationalities and races, but recognizes that: a. all humans are part of the same family, a fact which is more important than any of their differences; b. this family has one planet, and that one planet is small; c. they have one planet, it's small and it's endangered; d. there's just the

18

one, it's not very big, it's not very well, and if they don't save it, no one else is bloody likely to.[13] Thus, the global village. In this village, Tanzanian goat herders and Hollywood starlets are seen not as separate tribes, but as individual parts of an organic whole, with the same wants, needs, and long-range goals.

Simple, isn't it?

The Global Village, as explained by Minuetta Aka, from Grosch

There were several things I thought I understood before I got to Earth. I thought I knew what logic was. I thought I knew what rational behaviour was. I had a firm hold on the concept of truth. I was absolutely sure about the global village. After all, what was there to understand? Every life-form in the cosmos is born with the knowledge that it is part of the whole, the whole is part of it, and each is responsible to the other.

Then I arrived in America. I went to McDonald's. I watched television. I investigated the shops and supermarkets. Every store I went into sold goods with the images of something called 'Ninja Turtles' on them. I asked if these Ninja Turtles were some sort of national heroes — physicists, philosophers, or poets, figures deserving respect: as it turned out they were cartoon characters. I bought myself a baseball cap and a T-shirt with the silhouette of a palm tree and the word 'California' on it.

From there I was transported to Britain. I went

---

[13] As already discussed, many humans do, of course, believe that someone else is going to save it for them. This is because they haven't quite figured out where the centre of the universe is, and that they're not it.

to Liverpool, Bristol, Leicester and London.
Despite the baseball caps, Ninja Turtles,
skateboards and great number of McDonald's
restaurants, I knew I had left America because of
the weather and the fact that the phones never
worked. Nonetheless, by the time I got to
Leicester, I was a little confused. I was confused
because, except for a few architectural and
speech differences, it was difficult to tell any of
these towns apart. They all had the exact same
shops. The shops all had the exact same things
for sale. In London I bought a T-shirt with the
silhouette of a palm tree and the word 'Cornwall'
on it.

I went to Europe.

For the first three days, I was sure I must have
got my coordinates wrong and that I was actually
back in America. True, not that many people
were speaking English, but not that many people
seemed to be speaking English in America,
either. People were drinking Coca-Cola. People
were eating at McDonald's. American music
blared from the radios of Europe; American
programmes sizzled from its TV screens. The cars
were smaller, but the clothes were the same. I
wondered if this was normal, or if I were caught in
a time–space distortion, seeming to move, but
really standing still. In Berlin I ate a Big Mac and
bought a T-shirt with the silhouette of a palm tree
and the word 'Florida' on it.

I went East.

People in the East tend to look different to
people in the West, which went some way
towards quelling my rising panic that I was still in
my ship in the Groschian Galaxy, caught in a
quantum gap. There was something happening
here, but I wasn't sure what it was. Gingerly,
because of what seemed to be a perpetual state of

Humans now recognize that they are all part of the same family.

unrest in this part of the world, I crossed more continents.

In Africa, I drank Coca-Cola and listened to rock music. In India, I drank Coca-Cola and listened to rock music. In Indonesia, I drank Coca-Cola from a plastic cup with Ninja Turtles on it and watched repeats of 'Bonanza'. I bought a T-shirt with the silhouette of a palm tree and the word 'Bali' across the front. In Malaysia, I drank Coca-Cola and listened to rock music while eating crisps. But it wasn't until Singapore that everything fell into place.

I was sitting in McDonald's, wearing a T-shirt with the silhouette of a palm tree and the word 'Singapore' on it, and watching an American cop show on my Watchman, when a commercial came on. Several commercials. The first was for dandruff shampoo. A feeling of *déjà vu*, such as one sometimes experiences after travelling too many light-years, suddenly overcame me. And then I realized what it was. Though the actors had been Caucasian, I had seen this same commercial in Liverpool, Geneva and Akron, Ohio. The second commercial was for instant coffee. I had seen this one, not with Oriental actors, of course, but the same commercial, in Livorno, Madrid, Bristol and Helsinki. And then the third commercial began. It was for a soft drink. Hundreds of people were standing on a hilltop, singing about peace, harmony and one world.

I dropped my Egg McMuffin. I wasn't in an aberrant electron field. I wasn't experiencing starship lag. I was in the global village! The notion that I was experiencing this phenomenon first-hand hadn't occurred to me earlier, for the simple reason that there were so many places where one couldn't go — or couldn't go for long or with any guarantee of coming back — because of famine, war, terrorism, or an imaginative combination of one or more of these conditions. But now I understood. The global village here wasn't the same as everywhere else in the cosmos; it had nothing to do with the perception of self and society. It was a marketing ploy.

Do You Have What It Takes?

The majority of us are, of course, accustomed to travelling throughout the cosmos and know how to adapt and survive. Because of this, it would be easy to assume that a journey to Earth would be no more demanding than a journey to Infe Minor. But it would be a mistake. Life on Earth is simply not as easy to survive as life on a large planetoid of untamed wilderness and three months of night is.

Likewise, it would be wrong to assume that surviving life on Earth is merely a question of learning certain skills. It is more than that. Survival on this planet takes special qualities and instincts; qualities and instincts not possessed by all of us.

These are:

1. An over-active imagination. It is impossible to stress the importance of this too much. Many visitors to Earth return home gibbering wrecks simply because they failed to appreciate how weird things could become. If it would never occur to you to dismantle the Berlin Wall and then sell pieces of it as souvenirs; to name a restaurant Auschwitz; to let your cat sit in the armchair while you sit on the floor; to create diet dog food or the musical bird-bath; or to believe that your goldfish is the reincarnation of Elvis Presley, you probably aren't ready for the twentieth century.

2. An ability to improvise. Bearing in mind that no amount of advance study can really prepare you for market day in Little Bedleigh or Saturday night at the Kitty Kat Klub, the alien visitor needs to be able to think on his or her feet. Let's imagine a typical situation, the sort of thing that happens every day on Earth. You are going to Manchester from London. On the way to the train station, the bus suddenly detours from its regular route (the driver, perhaps, is depressed and fancies a little spin in the countryside) and the next thing you know you are on your way to Goring. The other passengers are enjoying the ride as much as the driver and have produced packets of biscuits and flasks of hot tea, but you,

23

who have an important appointment in Manchester, get out in Goring, thinking you'll be able to get a train back to London. But it's 6.00 p.m. on Tuesday. Because of a British Rail economy measure, there are no trains stopping at Goring in either direction after 5.00 p.m. on Tuesdays. Obviously, you think, you will have to take a taxi. The taxi-driver in Goring is having his dinner. 'It doesn't really matter, though,' his wife informs you. 'Al doesn't know how to get to London.' You must reach Manchester by midnight or risk returning to your non-human form. Although there is nothing wrong with your non-human form (you are considered quite attractive on Jhu Jhu 4), you can tell that it would not win you any friends in The Green Man public house. The question is: How would you get to Manchester? If your answer is, 'How the hell do I know?', then you probably lack the necessary resiliency for coping with tellurian emergencies.

3. An ability to make up your mind. On Earth, not only is quantity much more important than quality, but a lot of people make enormous amounts of money thinking of different ways to sell the same thing: for instance, sugar, carbonated water and caramel colouring (cola). You would think that one type of cola would be enough for any planet, but once again you'd be wrong. Humans have *hundreds* of different brands of cola. Not only that, but one brand may have half a dozen different varieties, all of which are pretty much the same. You can see, therefore, that a being who can't make quick decisions might spend thirty days in the cereal aisle of Sainsbury's, trying to decide between sixteen brands of cornflakes.

There is nothing quite like human ingenuity.

4. An ability to live with yourself. You certainly
    won't be able to live with them. They can't live
    with them, so how could you expect to? Take,
    for example, the experience of Anoushka Rioldi,
    a technician on the cruiser Panisha II. She tells
    of a Christmas dinner she spent with the Wilson
    family of Hollybush Road, Oxford. She'd been
    invited by Kate Wilson, Head of the Churchill
    Road Primary School, where Anoushka worked
    as a teacher. Anoushka had been looking
    forward to spending the most important
    Christian holiday with a real human family. This
    is how Anoushka recounts the day:

    Kate said that dinner would be at three, but that I
    should arrive around one to share in the
    festivities. I took this to mean carolling and
    egg-nog and perhaps a few traditional stories told
    around the crackling fire.

At 1.00 pm precisely, I rang the Wilson doorbell. When nothing happened after a few minutes, I rang it again. It was finally opened by a small and not particularly pleasant child who was stuffing chocolates into its mouth. I introduced myself and asked for Kate. The child slammed the door in my face. A few seconds later, Kate appeared and invited me in. 'You'll have to forgive my niece Ambrosia,' she said. 'You know what children are like at Christmas.' I lied and said I did.

As we walked towards the living room, Kate whispered to me not to say anything about the tree.

I said, 'Excuse me?'

She said that her parents hadn't spoken in six days because of the tree.

'They what?' I said.

'Six days,' she whispered. 'They had an awful row about it. My dad's very conservative, you know. He likes to chop down his own, but my mother's the one who spends the next nine months hoovering up the needles. So this year she insisted on choosing the tree.'

I was trying to follow this conversation, but I wasn't finding it easy. 'And they had a fight about it?' I queried.

'Bloody ten-rounder,' said Kate. 'Don't let on that I told you, but he's been sleeping on the sofa all week. They won't say a word to each other.'

We entered the living room. I was vaguely aware that there were people in the room, quite a few people actually, but my attention was grabbed by the tree. It was pink. I stared, although perhaps gawped is a more accurate description. I couldn't imagine why anyone would want a pink Christmas tree. In Los Angeles, perhaps, where, as you know, any

26

connection between life and reality is totally accidental, but not in Oxford, England. Had Mrs Wilson woken up one morning and leapt from bed with the happy cry, 'By George! What this house needs is a pink tree!'? Why? Furthermore, I couldn't even imagine anyone thinking of making a pink Christmas tree. Why? Perhaps the drug problem was worse than I'd been told.

'My goodness,' I remember saying, 'it's pink.' Kate kicked me — but too late.

Mr Wilson, who was sitting on the sofa with a red and gold paper hat on his head and a glass of whisky in his hand, stirred. 'Every bloody king and queen of England is rolling in their grave,' he informed me. 'The whole country's going to the Americans, of course. That's what the matter is. Everybody's eating hot dogs and wearing baseball caps. They've got American football on the telly.' He knocked back his drink. 'They'll be turning Buckingham Palace into a theme park next, I shouldn't wonder, that's what they'll do. Mark my words. Have Her Majesty selling postcards and charge a tenner to have your picture taken with Princess Di.'

Several people said, 'Dad, please, leave off, will you?'

'I will not leave off,' snapped Dad. 'It's my house. I can say what I please in my own home. It's still a free country, you know. They haven't taken that away from us yet. Bloody pink Christmas trees.'

Something very large and heavy fell to the floor of the kitchen.

'Oh my God,' said Kate. 'There she goes again.' She raced from the room.

I introduced myself to the rest of her family. 'Hello,' I said, 'I'm Anoushka. I work with Kate.' No one looked at me. The men were all wearing

27

paper hats, holding glasses of whisky, and
watching television. The women were wearing
paper hats and trying to stop the several
screaming children from hitting each other,
knocking over the tree, or eating more than four
chocolates at a time. Eventually, one of the
children noticed me standing in the doorway.
'Did you bring me a present?' she asked.

'Sharon!' scolded a woman I presumed must
be her mother. 'That's not polite.' She smiled at
me. 'You know what they're like at Christmas,'
she said.

This time I said, 'Yes,' with a little more
confidence.

Kate returned from the kitchen. 'I'm afraid
dinner's going to be a little late,' she apologized.
'Mum just threw the turkey on the floor.'

I didn't like to ask why.

No one else seemed interested in knowing.

Kate and I sat by the crackling fire. 'That's
funny,' I said as she passed me a box of
chocolates, 'there doesn't seem to be any heat
coming from this fire.'

'Of course not,' she laughed. 'It's electric.'

We sat and watched it glow. Time passed.
Except for the laughter from the television, the
crying and shouting of the children, the yelling of
the children's mothers, the occasional sound of
some part of dinner hitting the kitchen floor, and
the snoring that began when Kate's father passed
out in his chair, the room was oddly silent.

'Perhaps your mother would like some help
with the meal,' I suggested at last.

Kate shook her head firmly. 'Oh, no,' she said.
'Mum hates to have people in the kitchen with
her. She says it makes her nervous.'

I said, 'Oh.'

'She hates cooking,' confided Kate.

Again I said, 'Oh.'

'Especially on holidays.'

I switched to a polite, 'I see.'

'And of course,' Kate continued, 'she's in a
very bad mood because of the you-know-what.
That's why she threw the turkey on the floor.
Because she heard Dad banging on about the fall
of British civilization.'

I glanced over at the tree, shining brightly, if
pinkly, in one corner of the room. Two little girls
were busily pulling the tinsel from its branches,
while a third was adding wet paper napkins to the
decorations. 'Ought that cat to be there?' I asked.

Kate looked at me. 'What cat?'

'The cat that's climbing up the tree,' I said.

'Oh gosh, no,' said Kate, noticing for the first
time the yellow eyes peering out from between
the pink branches and the plastic snowflakes.
'Moggy!' she screamed. 'Moggy! Get down from
there!'

'I'll get her, Auntie Kate!' screamed a little
boy who was dressed as Superman and
brandishing a sword.

Instantly, the other children joined in. 'No, let
me!' they all shouted. 'Let me!'

Mr Wilson woke up when the tree fell on him.

Dinner was a strained, not to say strange,
affair. By the time it was ready, the men were
involved in the Christmas film on the telly, so
they ate in the living room. The rest of us, Mr
and Mrs Wilson, the three Wilson daughters, and
the six Wilson grandchildren all ate at the dining
table. It was the first time I realized that the
Wilson daughters didn't actually speak to each
other. That is, they asked to have the salt passed
and commented on the lumpiness of the gravy,
but that seemed to exhaust their conversation.
Their parents, who, of course, weren't speaking

to one another at all, talked a great deal more. If Mrs Wilson wanted the butter she'd say, 'Excuse me Kate, would you ask your father to pass the butter.' Kate would ask.

'Tell your mother I'm not through with it yet myself,' Mr Wilson would then say. Kate would tell her.

'What's he going to do, eat the whole bar?' Mrs Wilson would want to know. Kate would ask him.

'Tell your mother I can do whatever I bloody well want,' Mr Wilson would bellow. 'It's my house. They haven't taken that away from me yet.'

Things were hobbling along in that manner, when one of the boys threw a handful of cranberry sauce at his cousin. The cousin's mother yelled at him. 'Justin! Look what you've done. You're not having any dessert unless you apologize.'

Justin's mother took exception to the fact that her sister was yelling at her child. 'Why don't you mind your own business?' she inquired. 'I can discipline my son without your help.'

'Oh sure you can,' her sister shouted back. 'That's why you can't pay anyone to mind the little monster.'

'At least he doesn't look like a refugee from the Planet of the Apes!' raged Justin's mother.

The child who did look rather like a refugee from the Planet of the Apes burst into tears and fled the room. His mother picked up a drumstick and started hitting her sister about the head with it.

'Tell your mother I'd like to have the cranberries,' Mr Wilson said to Kate. The sister with the bits of turkey in her hair finally burst into tears herself and rushed from the room. The other sister then burst into tears and left the table. Then Justin threw a handful of mashed potatoes at his other cousin and she left the table in tears.

'Tell your mother she cooked this bird too long,' Mr Wilson ordered Kate. Kate told her.

'Tell your father the next old bird I roast for too long is going to be him,' said Mrs Wilson, and then she too left in tears.

By the time we reached the plum pudding, only Kate, Mr Wilson and I were left at the table. Kate put too much brandy on the pudding and set her paper hat on fire.

When all was said and done, however, the day actually did live up to my original expectations. Not only were the firemen wearing sprigs of holly in their helmets, but they sang 'We Wish You a Merry Christmas!' as they put out the fire on the dining-room table.

5. The ability to adapt to any situation and make the best of it. The operative word here is *any*. Most of us can easily adjust to a sudden turn in the colour of the weather or a change in atmospheric pressure, and few would be really flummoxed by having to share a compartment in a space shuttle with a gaggle of star surfers from Wanini. But what about a bus trip from Hastings to Newton Arlosh with a woman who has three cats in carrier bags with her? Or finding yourself outside Harrods just as the doors open for the January sales?

6. The ability to prepare for the worst even while you are hoping for the best. This means that when you find yourself at Delia Cockspur's New Year's Eve party, trapped beside the cheese ball by a gentleman with an extraordinary number of

stories about his time in India, you are able to think of six questions about the train to Jaipur at the same time that you are looking over his shoulder for a glimpse of a waitress with a tray of drinks.

7. Patience. Every life form has its epithet. The Bulwegeens, famous for their sense of fun, have been affectionately dubbed the quantum kidders. The Pps, legendary for their sharp, uncompromising intellects, are always identified as the critics of the cosmos. The Gundelions, honoured for their understanding of the nature of being, are our intergalactic gurus. Just so, it is easy to see why humans are known as the bureaucrats of the universe. A task that would take you a matter of minutes anywhere else in the cosmos — filling out an application for a building permit, for instance — can take not a matter of hours or even days on Earth but months or even years (unless you are, of course, in Russia or China, in which case you will never get the permit). That is why patience is so necessary. Ever since the ill-fated exploratory expedition of Reit-4 and DF30 from Xab99 (a planet, as you know, where everything runs so perfectly and efficiently that evolution has erased patience from the genetic make-up), all Xabians have been forbidden to travel to Earth. This is because Reit-4, laid off from work because of what turned out to be a computer error, went to sign on. He went on a Monday. By Wednesday, DF30 was worried about him and went to the DHSS office. Reit-4 was fourth in the queue. It was the fifth time he'd been in the queue. Everything went all right until he actually reached the desk. When he reached the desk, he was always sent to another window. He

would wait in the queue for that window. When he reached the window, he would be sent to another window.

'I don't believe this!' shouted DF30. 'You've been here three whole days! How have you managed not to lose your temper?'

'I've been reading a lot of bestselling paperbacks,' Reit-4 explained. 'It puts me right to sleep.'

DF30, who walked everywhere because she didn't have enough patience just to wait an hour or two for a bus, said she'd see Reit-4 at home. And, miraculously enough, Reit-4 managed to return home that evening. 'Well, at least that's over,' he said philosophically. And incorrectly as it turned out. His giro never came. He telephoned the office several times, but all that happened was they put him on hold. He went back to find out why he'd never received his money. This time he only had to wait four hours. He was told that his cheque was in the post. 'Let's be fair,' he said to DF30 when five days later his cheque had still not arrived. 'The clerk didn't actually say *whose* post it was in. Maybe it's coming through Holland.' He tried phoning again. Often he would be put through several different people, but always he would end up listening to the hum of silence while he read a Jeffrey Archer novel and drifted off to sleep. DF30 went down to the office to find out what was happening. They arrested her for disturbing the peace. Not only did they arrest her, but they lost her. She spent seventeen hours in a holding cell because someone mixed up her paperwork and sent it on to Chelmsford. Reit-4, of course, wasn't worried when DF30 didn't return that evening, because he assumed she was still in the queue for information.

8.   Endurance. Humans, of course, can endure almost anything. Look at the leaders they elect, the commercials they sit through, the hours they spend watching Sylvester Stallone movies and having their legs waxed. It makes sense, therefore, that if you're planning to spend any time on the planet you're not only going to have to be able to sit in traffic on the motorway for several hours without falling apart, you're also going to have to be able to survive real tests of mettle like listening to George Bush explain that he wanted to be President so that he could bring about world peace.

9.   The ability to lie. Humans can not only endure almost anything, they find it almost impossible to tell the truth. Obviously, this makes them a little untrustworthy. Don't lend them anything you would like to have back and don't tell them anything you would mind having blared through solar loudspeakers to the very edges of the cosmos, especially if they swear on the head of their sainted mother that they would never tell another soul. To further protect yourself, however, you will have to lie as well. Being the only person on a sizeable planet who is telling the truth all the time is not a position you want to put yourself in. People, being people, will take advantage of you. When they're not taking advantage of you, they'll be getting angry. You'll tell Sheila that you can't go to her masquerade party on Saturday because the thought of dressing up as a pea-pod gives you a headache and, anyway, let's face it, her parties are more boring than watching a darts tournament, and the next thing you know, Sheila's throwing her glass of cola at you and bursting into tears. If you insist on telling humans the truth all the time

— especially about themselves — you will have no friends but quite a few enemies. Humans are dangerous enemies because they work on the theory that if something awful happens to someone they don't like, it's as though something good has happened to them.

10. The ability to 'walk in the cosmos' — to see the beauty of the universe no matter where you are. To see, as one survivor did, a flower growing in an urban window-box and think, *how brave that geranium is to bloom where the soot and the acid rain fall and some drunken yob is likely to come along and pluck it on his way home from the pub.* To see, like another, the pulsating light of the disco and think of the star clusters of the outer nebulae. Or to watch five people try to divide the restaurant bill and be 'profoundly moved'.

11. A high boredom threshold. Humans are entertained by watching two people hit balls around a table with sticks. They'll sit in the sun for hours, excited by a tennis match (which is similar to being excited by watching Neptune rotate). They think that darts (which led the early explorer Humphrey Stasi, who spent hours in The Green Man in Putney watching it because there seemed to be a bit of bother in the streets at the time, to coin the phrase so popular throughout the universe, 'more boring than watching a darts tournament') is a sport. They read Jeffrey Archer. They go to the opera and listen to people singing in a language they don't understand. They dance to disco. They sing along with advertizing jingles. Clearly, humans have a boredom threshold larger than their solar system. Unless you can convince yourself that

going to a brightly lit fast food restaurant and eating a pre-made hamburger and a handful of chips is a pleasant way to spend thirty minutes of your life that isn't going to last for ever, you're going to have problems on Earth.

12. A sense of humour. You figure it out.

Dos and Don'ts for Aliens

Here are a few basic rules, which, if followed, will also help to ensure that you bring the minimum amount of attention to yourself and stay out of jail.

Never assume too much.

Always expect the worst.

Avoid becoming too closely involved with humans. As pleasant and even interesting as many of them are,[14] close (not to say intimate) contact is at best confusing and at worst fatal.

The minute someone tells you not to worry, begin.

Bring your own food, if possible.[15]

---

[14] Lucia Lipto, the cosmos-renowned philosopher and poet, once spent three very pleasant if largely intoxicated days discussing life, its meaning and its cosmic potential with the middle-aged William Shakespeare (though Lipto does say that Will got a little gloomy on port), and several alien explorers have reported extremely pleasing times spent with Albert Einstein, though Einstein never seemed to remember where he'd left anything.

[15] With one or two notable exceptions (like the olives of Italy), the food on Earth tends to fall into two categories: food that looks real but isn't (e.g. frozen dinners); and food that doesn't look real and isn't (e.g. ranch-flavoured nacho chips).

Don't drink the water. Especially not if it's bottled and expensive. Unless, of course, it comes from a planet whose environment is still user-friendly.

When asked — even begged — for your honest opinion (as in: 'No, I mean it, Abpu, what do you *really* think? You know you can tell me the truth.'), don't give it.

Never get into an argument with a small, elderly woman wearing an all-weather mac, a headscarf, and carrying an umbrella.

Never take sides in a domestic dispute.[16]

Never think that because something hasn't gone wrong yet, it won't.

Always count your change.

Remember: things don't have to make sense.

---

[16] One field researcher from Ektron Nine tells a story of coming upon two humans arguing on a street corner. He gathered from the fact that the female of the couple kept screaming, 'You leave my family out of this,' and the male kept saying things like, 'And as for your brother!' that they were husband and wife. Just as the Ektronite was about to pass them, the man started pushing the woman around. He shoved her into a lamp-post. He slapped her face. She started to cry. Humans, seeing this same scene, would think, oops, domestic squabble, and hurry on — or they'd think, oops, domestic squabble, and stop to watch — but Ektronites, commonly called the guardians of the cosmos, can't pass anyone in trouble without stopping to help. He stopped to help. He laid one hand on the man in a restraining fashion, and said, 'Excuse me, but I'm going to have to ask you to stop using physical force on this woman.' At which point, the woman shrieked, 'Get your filthy hands off my Larry, you bastard,' and started walloping him over the head with her handbag.

Furthermore, if things do seem to make sense, you have probably misunderstood the situation.

Never become involved in a discussion of politics, religion, the right way to boil an egg, or Jim Morrison.

Never assume that the way a thing is done is the best way to do it.

Don't think that because someone is smiling he must be friendly.

If, while out one night, a large man wearing the head of Nefertiti in gold around his neck should ask you what your problem is, don't tell him.

Don't believe anything you read in the papers.

No, nothing.

Remember, on this planet, art doesn't imitate life, life imitates commercials.

PANIC. Panic even when you think you shouldn't. Panic even when there seems no real reason to. Given the way things work on Earth, you can hardly go wrong.

What to Pack

In order to have a successful tellurian visit, you must arrive equipped for twentieth-century existence. Just as you wouldn't want to turn up on Foogoo Fonora without a dust shield, there are places on Earth where it would be inadvisable to land without a camera, or a gun, or a diary,[17] or something to do at night. It is especially important for the alien visitor not to bring attention to him or herself, but to blend into the background. The last thing

38

Always dress appropriately.

[17] One of the more interesting facts of human behaviour is that, though they don't, on the whole, really seem to do that much (go to work, go out to dinner, go to the dentist) they are obsessed with writing it all down. Most people carry a small book in which they keep track of everything they do every day of the year, as well as keeping a similar book at work, and a large calendar in the kitchen. Some anthropologists believe this is because humans have such bad memories. Others, however, argue that it is simply another manifestation of their fear of being forgotten. Not only are they terrified that everyone else is going to forget about them, they're afraid that they will too.

you want is to find yourself part of a documentary on UFOs: Fact or Fiction because you went to the beach without sun bloc, sunglasses and a handkerchief tied around your head.

The Basics

Aside from a wardrobe appropriate to your character and locale, if you are visiting Earth in human form you will need some or all of the following:

Keys

Not just keys, of course, but a lot of keys, preferably on a large and cumbersome ring (especially if you are in America, it is important that this ring should attach to the belt-loop of your trousers or jeans). A key-ring that plays music or makes the sounds of a gunfight is especially desirable. If you are planning to be around a lot of lawyers, accountants or corporate executives,[18] a key-ring that doubles as an electronic calculator, address book or dictionary is a good idea. It is additionally important that at least one third of the keys on your key-ring don't fit any lock that you know of.

A Wrist-Watch

This watch can be gold, platinum, brushed steel and

[18] This type of man goes in for something known as 'the executive toy'. To put it simply, the executive toy is an object that is expensive and completely useless. There are, of course, several billion things on this planet that are expensive and completely useless (battery-operated balls for your dog, the doorknob cover, lawn aerator sandals, the woodpecker toothpick holder, the electric candle, plastic flowers, etc.), and several billion things that are expensive and largely useless (solid gold taps, stretch limos, platinum cigarette lighters, diamond toothpicks, designer clothes), all of which may seem confusing to the beginner traveller. Executive toys are the ones that fit on the corner of the desk and have no function whatsoever.

gold, silver and turquoise, or even leather, but it must be large, tell the day, year and month as well as the time, be waterproof, shockproof, visible in the dark, and play 'La Cucaracha' or chime like Big Ben every hour on the hour. The more useless functions your watch can perform — giving the time difference between Beijing and Little Bradford, for instance — the more impressed people will be by it.

A Cellular Phone

A cellular phone is unnecessary in the Third World, where a normal sort of phone is a rare enough occurrence (and where no type of phone actually works for more than a minute and a half), but it is becoming *de rigueur* in the industrialized West. Women and primitives, who still largely live under the delusion that a car is no more than a means of transportation, do nothing in an automobile but drive, listen to the radio and hunt fruitlessly through the glove compartment for the registration or a tissue, but sophisticated Western men use their time in the car to shave and talk on the phone. It makes them feel important.

A Personal Stereo

People are hard to figure out. On the one hand, they hate to be alone. They are great believers in socialization. They spend most of their lives trying to belong to one group or another, and anyone who doesn't belong is treated as suspect.[19] You can sell them anything — a

[19] Anyone who isn't seen to be part of the group (and the group can be a neighbourhood, a workplace, a class, a club, a sports team, a country, or four guys who ride home on the same train every night) must be one of ten things: 1. a foreigner; 2. a traitor; 3. a witch; 4. antisocial; 5. a snob; 6. hiding something; 7. insane; 8. a sociopath; 9. a sexual deviant; or 10. an alien. Of these ten things, the only one you might ever be forgiven for is insanity.

Gone are the days when bringing home a woolly mammoth proclaimed your manhood.

three-headed toothbrush, flared trousers, the bouffant hair-do, instant tea, Ninja Turtle biscuits, inflatable shoes, *anything* — as long as you can convince them that everyone else has or wants one.

On the other hand, of course, humans like to think of themselves as individualists. They like their 'space' and their privacy. They don't like to be crowded or to have to spend a lot of time thinking about someone else. Each likes to think of herself/himself as unique and special.

Thus the personal stereo was invented. The personal stereo allows a human to be in a crowd and alone at the same time. For the alien it is an especial bonus, because it means that you can be in the shopping centre, where 'Raindrops Keep Falling on My Head' is being pumped through the tannoy, and be tuned into Metax Field emissions from Oopsala.

Bumper Stickers

Bumper stickers are another manifestation of the I Don't Want to Be an Outsider Syndrome. Bumper stickers immediately label and place you — even though, since you are passing through in a car, they are largely labelling and placing you for people who will never see you again (and don't actually see you the first time). Obviously, if you are not planning to drive a car, you won't need any bumper stickers; but if you are, you will. The most popular ones express allegiance: to a place — I ♥ Norwich; to a dog — I ♥ Golden Labradors; to a football team — I ♥ Manchester United; or to a car — I ♥ My Ford. The next most popular impart information: All Man; If You Can Read This You're Going to Hit Me, and Then I'll Hit You; God Votes Conservative; Baby, Retriever and Three Cats on Board; First You Work and Then You Die. The next invites you to join the group: Flash Your Lights for QPR; Shop Till You Drop; Honk If You Love Jesus.

If you don't have a car, T-shirts fulfil the same function.

Condoms

Fundamentally, condoms are a form of birth control. On Earth, however, they have a more important secondary purpose, which is to establish sexual prowess. Human males carry at least one condom around with them at all times, in case, as the idiomatic phrase goes, they 'get lucky' — and, more significantly, to give the impression that they are the sort of fellow likely to get lucky. The one thing a human male doesn't want to happen is to find himself with a woman who is willing to go to bed with him and no condom. By the time he has got into his car and driven to six all-night petrol stations and grocery shops, finally found a packet (in the wrong size) and arrived back home, his partner will be sound asleep and no longer in the mood.

Therefore, to maintain your credibility as a human male, it is necessary to carry at least one condom around with you in your wallet at all times. Be warned, however, when shopping for condoms, you will never find one marked 'small'. Condoms come only in large, extra-large, super-large, and should-have-been-a-stallion.

Tools

Men on this planet are expected to have an affinity for one kind of tool or another, because men, unlike women, are meant to be mechanically adept. It is assumed that men enjoy panelling the walls, laying patios, and changing the spark plugs and women don't; just as it is assumed that men are naturally good at that sort of thing and women aren't. The fact that none of this is true — most human males are less interested in rewiring the electricity or tuning the engine than a gekko would be, and many women like nothing more than to spend the weekend building an extension onto the house — does not change the fact that this is what people believe. DIY books and stores are, therefore, aimed at men. As presents, children are encouraged to give their fathers lug wrenches and their mothers electric tin-openers.

So, if you are going to be a man on Earth, you will need tools. Power tools are perennial favourites (they're large, heavy, cumbersome, and dangerous), but a good set of screwdrivers and spanners is a respectable start as well. Remember, you're never going to have to actually use them, you just have to leave them lying around. Although most people know at least one chap who has gone through the water pipes with the electric drill or taken off the tip of his thumb with the saw, it is likely that they all know the same two people, because no one else ever bothers. Most men, given a drill for Christmas, put up three shelves in the living room and then, when they fall down at two in the morning, never touch so much as a screwdriver again as long as they live.

Diet Books and Women's Magazines

Women on Earth are assumed to have different interests to men. Men are meant to be interested in making a lot of money, killing each other, building a wing on the house, and developing biceps; and women are meant to be interested in losing weight, looking as attractive as possible, and finding out how to improve their cooking and their embroidery, as well as whether or not they are too demanding of their families.

Anyone visiting the planet in the female form would therefore be well-advised to have a stock of appropriate reading material. Don't be daunted by the vast, and ever-increasing, number of books and magazines available; it doesn't really matter which one you choose. One diet book will tell you not to eat carbohydrates, one diet book will tell you to eat only tomatoes, one will advise you against fats, and the next will recommend a regimen of water and pineapples, but as none of them work for more than three days, it doesn't really matter which one you read.

Just so, not only is each women's magazine pretty much like the next, they are all like each other. Every Christmas issue gives its readers 'A Sumptuous Holiday Feast', 'Biscuits from the Past', 'Tips on How to Survive the Season', '101 Gifts You Can Make In Your Spare Time for Next to Nothing', and 'The Post-Christmas Diet'. Every June issue offers 'Getting in Shape for the Summer', 'Cool Meals for Sizzling Days', '101 Family Holidays You Can Afford', 'Best of the Bikinis', and the 'How Do You Know if He Really Loves You?' quiz.

Why do women — most of whom have no more interest in another recipe for pasta salad or instructions for sten-cilling furniture than most men desire to break their knees in rugby or lay a patio — read these magazines over and over and over again? They read them because the maga-zines that men read — filled with pictures of naked young women straddling stuffed toys, pictures of young men on steroids coated with vegetable oil and lifting a baby grand piano with one hand, or convoluted essays on the intimate life of the computer — bore them to tears. At least women's magazines have recipes, tell you how to crochet a sun room, and give you advice on removing grass stains.

Sports Equipment

The maintaining of a place at the back of the cupboard for a deflated football, a set of weights, a tennis-racket in need of re-stringing or an unused rowing-machine is an example of the efficient combination of nostalgia with myth, something people are extremely skilled at. The myth, of course, is that all men are natural sportsmen and like nothing better than to spend their Saturdays kicking a ball around in the mud and having their noses broken. The nostalgia comes from the fact that this is what they were encouraged to do as boys, so they think that they miss it (though what they really miss, of course, is being twelve).

Nonetheless, it is important to appear interested in the physical side of things. Not only do humans distrust too much thinking (which, presumably, is why they engage in it so seldom), but they especially distrust men who don't like to get bloody and sweaty in competitive sports, either as a participant or a spectator. They think that a disinterest in senseless violence and brute force is a sign of effeminacy. Any man who doesn't enjoy being kneed in the groin in the field or in the stands when the fight breaks out over the referee's decision was obviously too close to his mother as a child. The good news is that it's usually enough if you drink your tea from a mug with a team emblem on it and watch football on the telly on a Sunday afternoon, while you inhale beer and shout at the set.

Soft Pornography

You are not a man if you don't enjoy the sight of naked women. You would, of course, be outraged if any women you were close to — mother, sister, girlfriend, wife — suggested that she liked the idea of men looking at her naked body. That would make her a slut. But to find anything offensive in a topless teenager smiling out at you from your morning paper indicates a lack of appreciation of the female form and latent homosexuality. A calendar of models in wet T-shirts tactfully placed on the inside of your closet, or a few copies of *Playboy* left in the bathroom or under the carpet in the hall, will go a long way to convincing your associates that you are one hundred per cent male.

Weapons

There are still a few places on the Earth where every third man or boy you pass isn't carrying a concealed weapon. Some of these are places where every third man or boy you pass is carrying an unconcealed weapon, of course, but some are places where the men and boys wouldn't even dream of being armed. Most of the latter are small coastal villages, remote islands, or in Sweden.

Many extraterrestrials find the human preoccupation with small arms puzzling in a species that likes to think of itself as evolved. But, of course, they don't mean evolved in our sense of the word; they mean evolved from the club to the automatic with a silencer.

One has only to watch a few popular films to realize that what Man respects far above intellect, reason, or a good sense of colour is an ability to swing through a warehouse on an old piece of rope, cracking jokes while bleeding badly from a wound in the leg and slaughtering sixteen mercenaries with bad attitudes at the same time.

Thus, even though most men and boys have no intention of using the knives they keep in their boots, the chains they keep in their pockets, or the guns they keep behind the cistern (and indeed probably couldn't without permanent harm to themselves), it makes them feel better to have them. More manly. Important.

Many observers blame Hollywood.

Boris Sidvac, from the planet Vee Minor

I was with my friend Al Fieldstone one night, coming back from an afternoon of bird watching, when we decided to stop for a beer at The Green Man. It was one of those old-fashioned locals.

47

There was a football scarf draped over the till. There was a dartboard in the corner and the telly never worked properly. As you removed the bags of peanuts on the display card, the picture of a half-naked girl was revealed. It was what you'd call a rugged, man's sort of pub. It was a Saturday, so the place was crowded. I got the drinks while Al went to play a computer game.

Somehow, coming back with the drinks, I inadvertently bumped into a young woman named Sharon Cocoa. I spilled a little of my non-alcoholic lager on her skirt. 'Oh, I'm terribly sorry,' I said. 'It's just that it's so crowded...'

Sharon smiled. 'S'all right,' she said. 'I come here all the time.'

I went to stand behind Al, sipping my beer while the alien invaders wiped the screen with him.

Al was, by nature, a quiet, reserved sort of guy, steady and dependable. In fact, it's men like Al who often give visitors the impression that they're dealing with a sentient life form. 'Hey, this is a snap,' they say. 'That chap belongs to Greenpeace, named his dog Gandhi and has declared his flat a nuclear-free zone. I'm sure we can get along with these people after all.'

There were only two situations in which Al's veneer of a rational and sophisticated twentieth-century man dissolved to set free the grunting, hairy beast within. When Al was behind the wheel of his Toyota, especially in heavy traffic; or when Al was playing a computer game.

That evening, as I recall it, we weren't in The Green Man five minutes when Al's eyes became slow and fixed and sweat began to glisten on his forehead. He stepped on my feet several times, but didn't apologize so much as once, and he a man who normally apologized if he sneezed. I asked Al if he didn't want to continue the conversation we'd been having about house-martins and he told me to 'put a sock in it'.

Al was too involved in being beaten by the Alpha Beta Death Force to tear himself away, so I went up for the second round. Sharon Cocoa was at the bar. We smiled at each other. 'They're out of salt and vinegar crisps,' she told me conversationally, 'as usual.'

'That's a shame,' I replied, more out of politeness than anything else. 'They're my favourite.'

'Mine, too!' said Sharon. 'They almost taste real.'

We smiled at each other again, acknowledging the spiritual bonding that had just taken place. Sharon returned to her table, and I returned to Al. Al was shouting things at the Alpha Betas — things like 'Make my day you two-bit android', 'Eat gluons, sucker', and 'You're lucky you're behind that glass'. I handed him his beer. He drank it down in one swallow, wiping his mouth on the back of his hand. He burped.

Later, when I went to use the men's room, I met Sharon coming out of the ladies'. 'There's no paper in the loo,' she informed me. 'There never is.'

I offered to see if there was a spare roll in the men's. 'You're such a gentleman,' she said after she'd thanked me. 'I bet you don't come from around here.'

Somewhere past the third round and the twenty-eighth game, I looked up to find Sharon standing beside me. 'Who's your friend?' asked Sharon. Al's hair, usually neatly combed, was roughed up with sweat and tension. He had a five o'clock shadow and a thin trickle of blood flowed

from the corner of his mouth, where he had
bitten his lip in a moment of stress. He had rolled
up his sleeves and was staring at the screen with
the concentration of a trained killer about to see
whether or not he deserved that 'A' in Sneak
Attacks. The look she was giving him was
nothing like the look she had given me when I
fetched the bog roll for her. That had been the
look you would give a quantum equalizer should
you suddenly come upon it in the dairy case in
Safeway. The look she was giving Al, however,
was one of admiration and lust. 'He's *so* macho,'
I heard her say to herself. She moved closer to
him. 'I never understand these things,' she
breathed out loud, her voice suddenly little-girlish
and her hair much blonder.

Although any interruption by me had annoyed
Al no end, he turned to her with a wink and a sly
grin. 'They're actually very simple,' said Al.
Upon which statement Al, whose job was to write
computer manuals, thus rendering highly
complex and sophisticated programmes
intelligible and accessible to the layperson,
launched into an explanation of Invaders from
Alpha Beta that would have made it
incomprehensible even to its inventor.

Sharon was fascinated. She leaned over his
shoulder as he explained the difference between
the levels of play. 'Cor,' said Sharon, 'and I
thought chess was an intellectual challenge.'

It was at about that point that Sharon Cocoa's
boyfriend, Nick, joined us. 'What's goin' on 'ere?'
asked Nick.

'Nothin',' said Sharon.

'I was just explaining how to avoid being
trapped in a dead end,' said Al.

'S'at right?' said Nick. Nick's body was not
only about twice the size of Al's, it was obvious

from the way the flesh pressed against the arms
and torso of his T-shirt that he used it a lot more
than Al used his. Now and then, Al took his
body for a walk to the post office or gave it a
short ride on a bike, but Nick's body was clearly
used to lifting heavy metal weights and slicing
cement blocks in two with one swift stroke. Nick
laid one large paw on Al's shoulder and
squeezed. 'Well, if you want my advice, mate,'
said Nick, 'if I was you, I wouldn't go explainin'
nothin' to someone else's girl.'

I was about to say that, of course, that
sounded like very good advice indeed, when Al
cut me off by saying, 'Oh, yeah?'

Sharon said, 'Oh, Nick, for Pete's sake, stop
makin' a big deal out of nothing. I was bored
sitting by myself while you played darts, that's all.
And this gentlemen here,' indicating me, 'was
nice enough to get a loo roll for me, so I thought
I'd come over and have a chat.'

Nick growled.

I offered to buy him a drink.

'Get your hand off me,' ordered Al. And then,
turning to me, said, 'You'll buy him nothing.'

All three of us stared at Al. It was obvious to
me, who, after all, had been with Al during the
rather chilling Fight Over the Parking Space on
the High Street, that the combination of three
lagers and twenty-eight games of intergalactic
annihilation had seriously damaged his brain.

Al kicked over his chair. He rose to his full
five foot nine. He jabbed a finger in Nick's
over-muscled chest. 'Let's get something straight
here, cowboy,' said Al, sounding oddly like
Arnold Schwarzenegger, 'and that's that *no one*
pushes Albert Fieldstone around.'

'It's not true,' I tried to explain. 'Actually,
everyone pushes Albert Fieldstone around.'

Nick grabbed Al by the throat. 'I'm gonna punch the smile from your face once and for all,' he said, his enormous hand forming an equally enormous fist.

'Nicky,' said Sharon, 'Nicky, remember what the judge said last time.'

'Look here,' said I, 'surely there must be some civilized way of settling this. I mean, this whole thing is perfectly ridiculous. The young lady only came over to *talk*...'

'Oh, yeah?' Al sneered. 'You and what international armed force?'

'How about a mind game?' I suggested, resorting to the way differences are always sorted out on Vee Minor. 'There are five heat-radiating monsters from Glupto and three vapour-breathing Mugites, all of whom have to get to the opposite side of the particle shower ...'

Nick swung at Al.

Al pulled out a knife.

Later, at the hospital, I asked Al what he had been thinking of, pulling a fish-knife on a bruiser like Nick. 'You're lucky he was laughing so much that he forgot to smash your body into the bar,' I pointed out. 'I mean, a knife is bad enough, but a fish-knife! Surely if you're going to carry a weapon you should carry a flick-knife or a small sword. Something lethal.'

We were sitting in the corridor, waiting for someone to see the cut Al got when he stabbed himself with the fish-knife, trying to put it back in his boot. 'But that's just it,' sighed Al. 'I don't want to actually *kill* anyone. I just want to feel, you know, that I'm in control.'

'But Al,' I said, 'you weren't in control. You were practically drooling at the mouth. You were caught on the crest of a wave of violence and incipient sex. It was as though rabid baboons on heat had taken over your body.'

'No I wasn't,' said Al. 'I was just acting like a man.'

A Handbag

No one is quite sure why the quaint custom of calling these things handbags persists, when most of them are the size not of a hand but of a small suitcase.

The handbag is to the female human what the starship is to the intergalactic explorer. In it she keeps everything she will need to sustain life for as long as it takes her to get back home again.

Galet Galeta, from the Third Moon of Borzone

I'd been to the cinema and then to dinner with some human friends. It was quite late after the meal, and so I offered Kelly Acker, with whom I had spent most of the evening discussing Schroedinger, a ride home. Kelly accepted. When we got to her block of flats, I suggested that I accompany her to her door. 'It's all right,' said Kelly, 'I'll be fine on my own. I do have a Black Belt in karate, you know.'

'No, no,' I protested, not quite sure what her choice in clothing had to do with it. 'I'll see you safely in.'

We got to the front door of Kelly's building. Kelly opened her bag. I smiled at her. She smiled at me. She reached in for the keys.

After a few seconds she said to me, 'Galet, you wouldn't mind just holding a couple of things for me, would you? I can't seem to find my keys.'

'Of course not,' I said. I held out my hand. Into my hand she placed two small packets of tissues, half a packet of biscuits, a comb, a brush, a torch and three address books.

'That's better,' smiled Kelly. 'I think I feel them.'

But she didn't feel her keys. She felt two small jars of marmalade, a pair of scissors, a miniature spanner, and a spring coil. 'Hold these,' ordered Kelly.

'Are you sure they're not in your pocket?' I asked her.

'Of course not,' said Kelly. 'I *always* put them in my bag. In the change compartment, usually.'

'And they're not in the change compartment?' I persisted.

Kelly shook her head. 'I've got a needle and thread and some beads in there tonight,' she informed me. 'I guess that's why I couldn't fit the keys in as well.'

I might have asked her to go into a little more detail on the needle, thread and beads, but at that moment she brought a light bulb socket, several packets of artificial sweetener and a fork from her bag.

'Let me look,' I said. 'Perhaps it needs a fresh eye.'

Kelly handed me her bag. 'Suit yourself,' she said shortly.

I put the mound of things I was holding onto the floor and peered into the depths of Kelly's bag. Surprisingly enough, it didn't look as though anything had been removed from it. I took a deep breath and stuck in my hand. I pulled out a small container of orange juice and several batteries.

Kelly pounced on me eagerly. 'You're a genius!' she cried. 'I *knew* I had those batteries somewhere!'

I brought out a plastic cup, a jar of instant coffee, a pair of bikini bottoms, a scarf, two wallets, and a bar of chocolate.

Kelly snatched the bottoms away from me.

'My God,' she laughed, 'I've been looking for those since last June!'

'Ouch!' I screamed as something bit my finger. 'What on Earth is this?'

Kelly laughed. 'It's a mousetrap, of course. What did you think it was?'

I looked down. 'Is there a mouse in there, too?'

Kelly laughed again. 'Of course not,' she said. 'What a silly idea.'

I removed a small stuffed squirrel, a pair of sweat socks, two pairs of tights, a make-up bag, another make-up bag, a shower cap and a paperback copy of *War and Peace*.

Kelly leaned against the wall. 'You must be able to see them now,' she said.

I gave the bag a shake and looked in. 'You're right!' I cried, the joy of relief causing me to shout. 'I see them! I see them!' I pulled out a set of at least fifteen keys.

'That's not them,' said Kelly.

I froze in mid triumphant shake. 'You what?'

'Those aren't them,' she repeated.

'Whose are they, then?'

Kelly shrugged. 'Damned if I know,' she smiled. 'I've had them for years.'

'That does it,' I said. 'I'm dumping everything onto the floor.' I dumped. Gloves, a journal, a doorknob, several letters and post cards, photographs, news clippings, aspirin, plasters, cassettes, used tissues, Happy Birthday napkins, several crisp wrappers, a hat and a broken picture frame all tumbled to the ground. No keys.

'Now that's funny,' said Kelly. 'I was sure they were in there.'

'No you weren't,' I said, a little snappily. 'You were sure they weren't in the change compartment.'

This look came over Kelly's face. She reached

into the change compartment. 'Well, what do you know?' she smiled, holding up the keys. 'They were in there all the time.'

Make-up

Women wear make-up because, for some reason, they're convinced they look better with a little blob of blue on their eyelids, or a face that is one shade darker than their neck, than they do without the blob of blue, or if their neck and their face are the same colour.

The primary thing that the visitor must remember about make-up, however, is that it is never thrown out. You buy it, you use it, then you put it in a drawer. If you don't have a free drawer that will accommodate all the make-up you've accumulated over the years, then put it in a box under the bathroom sink. A woman who doesn't wear make-up and doesn't have at least a dozen old lipsticks, eyeliners, blush pots and mascara wands stashed away in the bed- or bathroom, is assumed to have either homosexual tendencies or a poor self-image. In the first case, men will constantly be trying to seduce you, convinced that the only reason you don't like men is because you haven't slept with them; in the second you'll find yourself reading a lot of women's magazines.

Credit Cards

It is possible to live on the Planet Earth without a credit card, but not easily. Ever since its inception, the credit card has grown in popularity until today it is more popular even than money. And why not? It's easier to carry, replaceable if lost or stolen, far more versatile, and much more convenient.

Not, of course, that there aren't drawbacks.

Misla Mixla II, from Space Station 34559

Every day during my stay in Surrey, there would be three things in my post for me, without fail.

The first would be a request for money to help save an endangered animal, feed a starving people, or provide food and shelter for refugees displaced by war/drought/hurricane/plague/or all of these things.

The second was a letter that began: 'Congratulations Mr Mixla and Family! You have won either a million pounds or a silver-plated bun warmer!'

The third was the offer of a credit card.

It was several months on Earth before I realized that I was the only creature on Badger Crescent who was supporting 350 charitable organizations, collecting silver-plated bun warmers, and without a credit card. 'You really should get one,' everyone told me. 'I wouldn't know how to live without mine. They're easy to carry, easy to use, convenient, flexible, mean you never have to do without just because you're a little short of cash, and they can be replaced immediately if stolen or lost.'

What I didn't realize, however, was that the most revolutionary thing about the credit card is that you can run up hundreds of pounds' worth of goods on it without ever leaving home. Books. Holidays. Theatre tickets. Sheets. Gold chains that are reproductions of ancient Egyptian jewellery. Wellies for the dog. A hoover for the cat. Porcelain miniatures. Scenes from Dickens in glass paperweights.

Before I knew what had happened, I was not only the owner of two tickets for *Phantom of the Opera* in 1995, a plastic bird-bath that looked like a sunflower, two sofas, a weeping lamp, a

The credit card allows humans to purchase everything they need from the comfort of their own homes.

scallop pin that beautifully captured Nature's design in eighteen-carat gold, a trip to see the Amazon before it was gone completely, and a machine that simulated mountain climbing in the privacy of my own home, I was also hopelessly in debt.

My neighbour, Desmond, scoffed at the state of panic this threw me into.

'What are you worried about?' laughed Desmond. 'The global economy is based on debt. Debt's what makes the world go round.'

'But how can I live like this, Desmond?' I argued. 'I owe thousands and thousands of pounds.'

'So what?' asked Desmond. He shrugged. 'Everybody's in debt, except the people who are too poor to get credit, of course. They're not in debt, they just don't have anything.'

'But I'll never be able to pay it all back.' Panic was making me forget that logic is as useful on

Earth as an electric Ninja Turtle toothbrush on X-241.

'Do you think Brazil's going to pay it back? You think Ethiopia's going to pay it back? You think Nigeria's ever going to get a clean credit rating?' Desmond waved away my concern. 'Nobody pays it back, Mis. That's the beauty of it.'

'Never?' I repeated, imagining spending the next 200 years on Badger Crescent, paying my five pounds a month minimum.

'Of course not,' Desmond chuckled. 'You just pay the interest.'

I'd only been in Surrey a few months, and couldn't get out of the habit of reason. 'But if I just pay the interest, I'll pay for what I've bought a hundred times over and still never pay for it.'

'You've got it,' said Desmond.

'But that means that billions of pounds a year must be spent on nothing. On lining the pockets of the credit card companies, when it could be spent on solving some of the world's problems.'

Desmond shook his head. 'You could put it like that.'

'Plus,' I squeaked, panic causing my voice to change frequency, 'plus, I'll never be free.'

'You and Guatemala,' said Desmond.

The City

London. Paris. New York. Barcelona. Moscow. Geneva. Los Angeles. Berlin. Liverpool. Glasgow. Minneapolis. Manchester. Reading. Just to speak the name of a tellurian city is to conjure up images of romance, excitement, glamour and beauty. Newark. Delhi. Johannesburg. Lima. Belfast. Beirut. Calcutta. Detroit. Or, alternatively; violence, bloodshed, poverty and oppression.

The theory behind the tellurian city, like the theory behind nuclear deterrents, is simple and basically sound. Theoretically, the city is a centre of commerce, culture, and population. It offers opportunities for both economic and personal achievement and diversification that would be impossible in the countryside or suburban development. Not so theoretically, cities, because of this concentration of people and resources, are either always under siege; in the grip of riot, street warfare, or terrorism; or simply overpriced, overcrowded and hotbeds of crime.

It is necessary, therefore, for the extraterrestrial tourist to prepare gingerly and carefully for even the short-term stay.

Attitude

You could bring bullet-proof clothing, small arms, a cache of grenades, two Rottweilers and a bodyguard with you to any city on the planet, but, in the end, what good would it do? Practically none. You might still be mugged waiting for a bus. Or blown up on the Tube. Or conned out of your watch and your trainers by a twelve-year-old with big eyes and a sad story. For no matter how polished your manner, extensive your knowledge of the language and customs, or general pleasantness, in London they'll ignore you, in Paris they'll be rude, in Calcutta they'll beg, in Rome they'll shout at you, in Bogota they'll try to sell you drugs, in Bangkok they'll try to sell you a girl, in Johannesburg you're likely to be shot, and in New York they'll be rude, ignore you, shout at you, beg, try to sell you drugs or a girl, and then they'll shoot. The only thing that you can bring that can possibly help you in a tellurian metropolis is an *attitude*.

'What sort of attitude?' you probably want to know. 'A good attitude? A bad attitude? An attitude of openness and curiosity? The attitude of a leopard spotting a man with a gun heading towards it?'

A human attitude.

The human attitude is best typified by the concept of compassion. People want to be seen to be humane. To be

60

humane is to be compassionate; to possess the best qualities of mankind: kindness, tenderness, sympathy and mercy. For example, you come upon someone begging on the street. A buffalo coming upon some poor wretch begging on the street would simply walk right by. A·lion might think about dinner. The average wood-pigeon would get out of range. But the humane response would be to stop and help, to offer some succour, no matter how small or how futile, to reaffirm the connection between man and man.

The humane response, but not necessarily the human one.

Not that the human won't want to stop and help. He will. He will think to himself, that could be me. He will think to himself, poor bastard, six kids, an aged mother, and no job for twelve months. His heart will lurch. Imagine sitting in a tunnel in the Underground, playing the theme tune from 'Bonanza' on the flute to make a little money to feed you and your dog, he will think. He might even remember the words of Jesus Christ, who said, 'What you do unto the least of these you do unto me.'

But then he will think again. Wait a second, he'll say to himself. How do I know this fellow really has six kids, an aged mother, and is unemployed through no fault of his own? Maybe he only has two kids. Maybe his mother is as fit as a fiddle and runs a very successful bed and breakfast in Swansea. Maybe he hasn't worked for twelve months because he's lazy or he's one of those .union agitators. Hang on! he tells himself. So what if he can play the theme tune from 'Bonanza' on the flute? I can play 'Heart and Soul' on the piano, but you don't see me sitting on the dirty floor trying to con people out of their hard-earned cash. He probably only brings the dog along for sympathy. It probably isn't even his dog. If it is his dog, I bet he doesn't treat it well.

And thus, with no visible effort, the human can be compassionate and callous at the same time. What an attitude!

'Hold on a moment,' you say. 'Just wait a minute. What happened to the wisdom of Christ?'

In the immortal words of the poet:

> *You know they refused Jesus, too.*
> *He said, 'You're not him.'*[20]

The Suburbs

The suburbs are to the city and the countryside what purgatory is to heaven and hell. Neither rich in museums nor brambles, the suburbs, lacking in both urban industry and culture and rural beauty, are the place in between. In this case, the place with tract housing, superstores, shopping centres, and commuter railways.

Net Curtains

People in cities enjoy an anonymity that can only come from having too many humans in too little space for too long a time. It makes them incurious. They might look up if they hear someone screaming nearby, but they won't rush to their windows to see if it's her in the back having an orgasm or the chap next door throwing things out the window again. Similarly, people in the country usually like to keep a few miles between them and their nearest neighbour, which makes it difficult for them to set their clocks by the time the folks next door have dinner or let the cat out.

But people in the suburbs live one on top of the other and side by side. Even if humans weren't naturally curious creatures, interested in the habits, secrets and furniture of others, it would be difficult for anyone in the suburbs to ignore what's going on next door or at the back, when next door or at the back are only feet and a layer of brick and plaster from their own front room.

---

[20] Dylan, Bob, 'Bob Dylan's 115th Dream', *Subterranean Homesick Blues*, CBS Records, 1964.

It was the British, of course, private to the point of secrecy, and reserved to the point of constipation, who invented the net curtain. The net curtain lets in the light but keeps out the prying eyes of passers-by and neighbours. More than that, though, the net curtain allows one to watch what everyone else on the street is doing without being too obvious about it. For the British are not just private and reserved. Raised in a society that discourages the personal question or direct statement, they are bloody curious as well. *Why do the Brynmores put all the upstairs lights on at eight o'clock every evening? Who is the gentleman in the grey suit who comes for dinner on Sunday? Where does Mrs Sorrell go every Thursday at one o'clock? Was that a new cooker that arrived last week or was it a fridge?*

Interestingly enough, however, it wasn't the British who invented the mirror that attaches to the top of the inner window-frame, allowing one to observe the street without so much as appearing behind the net.

'No?'

No. It was the Dutch.

Like nuclear energy, the suburbs seemed like a good idea.

A Television Set

Many a passing alien, though easily coming to grips with motorways and roundabouts, joggers, electronic tills that never work, dogs in baby buggies and the concept of peace through war, still ask the question: 'What did humans do in the evenings before there was television?'[21]

Those who stay in the suburbs know that the answer to that question is: 'Not bloody much.' In the city you can stand in a queue at the cinema for a couple of hours to pass the time, and in the rural outback you can watch a

---

[21] Arelia Po, the noted Inner Utian political analyst, maintains that there are three reasons for the invention and subsequent domination on tellurian life of the cathode-ray tube:

1. To protect the establishment and prevent possible insurrections. To support this argument, Arelia points out that revolutions on Earth occur in countries where a majority of the population owns less than one set per family, and where the reception is bad and programmes are limited to newscasts, documentaries and repeats of 'Bonanza'. As the great American President, Ronald Reagan, once said: 'They're not going to be worrying about the inequalities in the distribution of wealth when they can be worrying about who shot J.R.'

2. To sell snack foods. Before the advent of television there was no need — and certainly no demand — for pizza crunchers, corn sticks, just-like-potato crisps, cheese-flavoured popcorn, or sour cream tortilla chips. But now people need something to do while they're watching a film for the fourth time, and eating imaginary food (i.e. food that could never exist in nature) is it.

3. To sell everything. Or, to put it another way, television was the invention of a clever advertizing copywriter who realized that he could have himself a very nice lifestyle if he could come up with something that would actually *require* a perpetual run of ads. The ideal of course, and the long-range goal of the advertizing industry, would be to have one channel that shows nothing but commercials twenty-four hours a day, uninterrupted by anything as distracting as an actual programme.

meteor shower, but in the suburbs there's either lawn-mowing by candlelight or television. Therefore, if you're planning on visiting friends in the suburbs (no one, not even humans, visits the suburbs for any other reason, unless, of course, they're lost), bring a TV. Bring two and a video, so they won't even suspect that you might be from out of town.

The Countryside

City people live under the illusion that if anything is going to happen on the planet, it is going to happen beneath the bright lights and noise pollution of a metropolis.

Rural people know better. They know that if anything *really* important is going to happen — the arrival of ghosts, spies, demons, witches, elves, or Nazis from Outer Space, for instance — it is going to happen in the remote, un-populated countryside, where there is room to park a spaceship or call up the Devil.

For this reason, rural people tend to be a little sus-picious and slow to warm. They notice strangers before they arrive. They wonder where they've come from and why. Living in close proximity to nature (which is un-reliable at best), and knowing that outsiders only come to the country when they want something (e.g. to buy your land cheap before you discover that the government wants to run a motorway through it), people in the country don't trust anyone they haven't known for at least two gener-ations.

You'd be well-advised to go prepared.

A Dog

A dog will go a long way towards gaining you accept-ance. It will also make you less conspicuous, unless it happens to be wearing a rhinestone collar and a T-shirt that says I ♥ To Bark.

The Beach

Besides sun bloc, a cooler filled with cola or beer, a large
towel that looks like a can of cola, sun-glasses, white stuff
for your nose, enough food for two or three days, a radio,
a spare swimsuit, a robe, a change of clothes, goggles and
swim fins in case you actually can or want to go in the
water, you will need a thick paperback novel, otherwise
known as the Beach Novel.

Even in the outer layers of infinity, where things can
sometimes be a little weird, the written word is normally
reserved for the communication of important ideas,
concepts, information, or stories. Reading is considered a
serious pursuit, a participant rather than a spectator sport,
requiring attention, energy and imagination.

On Earth, however, reading is something that is done
on the beach. Every summer, thousands of people who the
rest of the year limit their reading to the television section
of their daily paper and the instructions on how to open
the milk carton, go off to the shore or to the hotel pool
with the usual trunk of equipment and a 1,000 page novel.

The Beach Novel concerns either four college room-
mates who meet again twenty years later, very rich people

Going to the beach does not necessitate getting wet.

who behave badly, very poor people who behave very well until they become very rich, or four college room-mates who meet again twenty years later. Because these books are intended for reading on the beach — when the reader needs something to do between turning over, going for a quick dip, and eating lunch — they are written so that the bather can open one on any page and know within a few sentences what the plot is, what the story-line is, and how it will all turn out. As well as being convenient, this is also economical. Since everything about these novels is identical except the names of the characters, a person can bring the same book to the beach year after year and never know the difference.

Chapter Three

Man: What Is It Exactly?

No one knows for sure.

Man is less intelligent than the dolphin, less loyal than the dog, less attractive than the cat, less fun than the otter, more treacherous than a hooded cobra and physically inferior to almost everything except the turkey. His idea of progress was to graduate from the rack to the neutron bomb. He is clever when he wants to be,[22] but emotionally unstable. What other advanced life form, for instance, would napalm whole villages without blinking an eye, and then burst into tears when Bambi's mother is shot?[23]

From just an evolutionary point of view, there seems little advantage in allowing a species that has made an art form of messing up its own water supply to dominate an entire planet. Some horrible mistake must have occurred. You can imagine the Earth's creator watching as the slimy things began to slither from the primal swamp. 'Hmmmm,' says the Earth's creator. 'I'd better keep an eye on that one there, it seems to have a bit of an attitude.' Time passes. The slimy things have become hairy and are swinging through the trees. 'Hmmmm,' says the Earth's creator. 'I'd really better watch that guy. His attitude's

---

[22] On a planet such as Dupu Beleezer, cleverness is a term applied to anyone who can manipulate time and space; on Uc, to a creature who can transform matter; on Sizzle Qwo, to star surfers. On Earth, you are clever if you invented a new hamburger, or a gadget for sealing plastic bags, or can level miles of irreplaceable jungle, making extinct hundreds of species of plant and wildlife, and still win an award for your concern about the environment.

becoming a problem. Look at the way he pushes the little ones around.' More time passes. They're out of the trees now, and running loose on the ground. 'Whoa,' says the Earth's creator. 'I'd better do something about that chap with the sloping forehead who keeps trying to stand on his back feet. If he had half a brain he might be dangerous.' But instead of putting him back in the pond as intended, the creator was distracted by something (a natural disaster, perhaps, colliding planets in another galaxy...) and, in the confusion, Man got half a brain. Good news for him, not so good for everything else.

But there is, of course, no point imagining how much more tranquil and understandable things would be if the dolphin or the elephant or Jackson's chameleon were in charge. No point in picturing a planet free of indestructible plastic bags, three-mile shopping centres, repeats of 'Allo! Allo!', and 'The Benny Hill Christmas Special'. Man bludgeoned his way up the evolutionary ladder, and that's where he's going to stay. The question for the visitor is: What makes him tick?

'Well, that's easy,' you say. 'I've read the *Reader's Digest Great Books of the World*. What makes Man tick are his intellect and his heart.'

And his reproductive organs, but we'll touch on that later.

---

[23] Bambi is a deer. Not a real deer, of course. A cartoon deer. While still a fawn, Bambi is orphaned when his mother is shot by a hunter. No matter where this cartoon is shown, the audience starts to cry when Bambi's mother hits the ground. Even if they've seen it before. If Bambi were a real deer they would be more philosophical and less emotional. 'That's life,' they'd say. Every autumn men dress in padded jackets and red hats, arm themselves with shotguns, and go into the woods to blow the brains out of real deer. This is called sport. They wear red hats so that they won't shoot each other by mistake (though they often shoot each other anyway). They have the heads of the murdered deer stuffed, and they put them on the walls of their homes. This is called interior decoration.

Reason

Here is an example of human logic. Country A, a defender of truth, justice and democracy, stands against everything represented by country B. Country B is a ruthless dictatorship whose citizens live in a state of terror and oppression. Country A and country B are virtually at war, though not openly, of course. But country B conducts terrorist attacks on innocent civilians to undermine country A, and country A supports, through arms, monies and manpower, the enemies of country B. Country A, very busy defending truth, justice and democracy, is also virtually at war with country C. The government of country A doesn't like the government of country C, even though it was democratically elected, doesn't oppress and slaughter its citizens, and carries on no terrorism against Country A, or anyone else for that matter. Country A wants to change the government of country C. But to do that, they need money. Money that doesn't have to be declared and can't be traced, because what they want to do (though in a good cause: the cause of freedom) is illegal and may upset some of its own citizens. So what do they do? What would you do?

'How do I know?' you ask. 'I have no idea what I'd do. I would never have got into this mess in the first place.'

That's because you're not human. If you were human, you would have got into this mess, and to get out again, what you would do, is you would secretly sell arms to country B.

'Hang on a nanosecond,' you say. 'I wouldn't do that. Country B is going to use those arms to fight *me* and my allies.'

Yes, that's true.

'And country C is more in tune with my ideals anyway.'

Yes, that's true, too.

'So where's the logic in that?'

It was one of the most popular presidents in the history of the United States who publicly declared that trees, one of the most beneficial and necessary creations on the planet, caused air pollution.

'What does that have to do with selling arms to your enemy?'

There's no logic in that, either.

Love

Artumo Seselked, from the planet Tu

Long after I'd discovered the canals of Britain, I heard a story from a fellow I met at a fuelling station on the fifth moon of Sha. We were sitting around, comparing experiences. I told him about the cow. 'To this day I don't know what it was about me that made them so angry,' I said. 'I hadn't done anything to them, I hadn't threatened to do anything to them, all I'd said was, "Hello there". Lord love a lepton, they were *smiling*!'

This fellow, whose name was Archie Phu, put down his glass with a philosophical sigh. 'That's nothing,' he said. 'Wait till you hear what happened to me.

'I was living in England at the time,' said Archie, 'researching non-telepathic means of communication, when I inadvertently became involved with Miss Emily Stone.'

'Involved?' I prodded. 'How involved?'

Archie broke a bku chip in two and gave me a look similar to the one Einstein wore when the full reality of the atomic bomb hit him. 'Engaged,' he whispered.

I couldn't hide my surprise. 'To a human? You were emotionally bonded to a human? How did that happen? Hadn't you heard of the Dos and Don'ts for Aliens?'

Archie sighed. 'Of course I had. But this

non-telepathic communication is tricky.' He sighed again. 'What happened was that we shopped in the same grocer's.'

I looked interested, but made no comment.

He went on. 'One evening she asked me to take something down from the top shelf for her.' He gave me a defensive look. 'So of course I did. I couldn't refuse, could I?'

I looked interested, but made no comment.

'Another way humans resemble electrons,' said Archie, 'is that even when you think you know what they're doing, you don't. One minute I was getting the recycled kitchen roll down for her and the next we were saying hello to each other on the street, stopping to chat at the bus stop — you know how one thing just seems to lead to another down there.'

One day two sticks rubbed together and a tiny flame; the next the microwave oven and the lukewarm baked potato.

'Finally,' said Archie, 'she asked me to the cinema one Friday night.' That Einstein look came into his eyes again. 'Naturally, I told her that I wasn't going to be in town for very long and that I wasn't looking for a relationship.'

'And what did she say?'

'She said she understood perfectly and that we could just be friends.'

'Kiss of death,' said I.

'Exactly,' said Archie. 'Before I knew what had happened, I had completely ignored the Don't Get Involved rule, and Miss Stone was taking me home to meet her parents, Ivy and Jack. She said that she'd never met anyone like me before, which was obviously true, and that she loved me more than life itself. She said that I gave her existence meaning. She said that without me she would die. She said that the only thing she wanted was my happiness. Nothing else mattered. I suspected that if she knew what I really looked like back home — that is, if she found out about my ears and my external lungs — she would probably change her mind, but there was no way I could risk bringing attention to myself like that, so I broke off our relationship as gently as I could. I told her that I respected and cared for her, but that I was a traveller both by nature and profession and not about to settle down in Streatham. Miss Stone's response to my honest explanation and offer of friendship was to sneak into my flat while I was out and pour black enamel paint over all my personal belongings. When I came home and tried to stop her from torching all my clothes and papers, she attacked me with a bread-knife. Thereafter, she followed me around, turning up when least expected to yell and scream and publicly berate me. She sent me threatening letters. Then she sent me tear-stained letters of undying love. She chained herself to the gate outside my building. She threw red paint all over a woman she saw me talking to by the frozen foods, because she thought I must be seeing her (I wasn't, she'd wanted to know if I'd ever tried the potato puffs). She telephoned me at all hours of the day and night, by turns cheerful and affectionate and hysterical and abusive. When I pointed out to her that she seemed to me to have a peculiar idea of achieving my happiness, the only thing she wanted in the world, she said I was a cold, unfeeling and selfish reptile and threw a set of cast-iron cookware at me, piece by piece, concussing me with the Dutch oven. She held my hand and cried all the way to the hospital. As soon as I was released, she tried to run me down with her car.'

'Good grief,' I said. 'That's worse than the cow.'

Archie sipped his drink reflectively. 'I can't help feeling it was a mistake that they ever learned to talk,' he said.

Hate

As human emotions go, hate is a lot more reliable than love. At least one knows where one is with hate, has some idea of what to expect. Not, of course, that hatred doesn't often have its own irrational basis.

Megoyd, from the planet Q8

I was on a one-being exploration of twentieth-century London, when something went wrong with the electrics in my personal transport system. What happened was, I was crossing Charing Cross Road, when a rather large car, moving against the traffic light, nearly ran over my toes. In a civil but admonitory manner, I tapped the bumper and called out, 'Oi! You're meant to stop!' The next thing I knew, the driver's door opened and I was whacked on the back of the head with a briefcase. Something happened to the electrics when I fell, because when I came to, I was in the middle of nowhere when I should have been on Oxford Street, purchasing a baseball cap with an elephant head on it and a T-shirt featuring the silhouette of a palm tree and the legend 'Scotland'. In the distance, I could see some sort of primitive dwellings. There wasn't a satellite dish in sight. I went to find out where I was, and when. As it turned out, I was in Oregon, in 1853. But, of course, I didn't discover that until I was being tarred and feathered and run out of town on a rail.

The town was small. It had one shop which also served as bar, post office and court-house. As I approached it, I could hear talk and even laughter. I walked through the doors. The room went silent. Everyone turned to stare at me. I was the only person in the room who wasn't white (Q8s, of course, are normally blue, but this becomes almost mocha in the Earth's atmosphere). Besides that, I was the only person in the room wearing surfer shorts, a T-shirt advertising a popular British lager, pump-trainers with neon-orange laces, and a badge that said, I'm Only a Visitor Here, What's Your Excuse? And I was clean and didn't smell like old socks that had been under the bed in a plastic bag with an apple core for the last six months, which also caused me to stand out somewhat. My hair was in several dozen small plaits. I smiled. 'Well, hello there,' I said. Somewhere to my left, a pin dropped. I really wished I wasn't wearing the gold hoop in my left ear. 'Nice day,' I continued. I began to wonder if, perhaps, the problem was that none of these people spoke English. In French, I asked for a glass of water. In Spanish, I asked for a glass of water. In Norwegian and Mandarin, I asked for water. Nothing happened.

And then, all at once, a deep, unpleasant voice broke the silence. 'He's a foreigner,' it said. And then, in case there was any doubt in anyone's mind, added, 'There's nothin' I hate more than foreigners.'

So they did speak English.

'Whaddayathink?' someone behind me asked of someone else. 'You reckon he's some sort of Injun?'

'I hate Injuns,' said the someone else.

'He ain't no Injun,' said a third voice. 'He's a runaway slave.'

75

A man whose skin was the same colour as his boots (though probably not naturally) spat in the corner. 'I hate runaway slaves,' he said.

'Look at the way he's dressed,' said a second spitter. 'That's what I hate. Decent people don't dress like that. You think he's one of those, you know, whaddayacallits?'

'His hair's funny,' said yet another voice. 'Are you sure he's not an Injun?'

'I bet he ain't even got a prick,' said someone else.

'I bet he ain't no Christian either,' said the man whose skin and boots matched.

'Of course he ain't no Christian,' said a gentleman who was gulping something that looked like fuel from a bottle, 'he's one of them foreign queans.'

'I really hate niggers,' said a large man with no teeth.

'Not as much as I hate Injuns,' said the fellow with what I hoped was a small animal hanging from his belt.

I wasn't sure if this was typical social intercourse in this part of the world, or if it could be said that the mood of the group was ugly and getting uglier. Perhaps, I thought, it was time I spoke up. I cleared my throat. 'Er . . . um . . . excuse me chaps,' I said, 'but I am neither an Indian nor a runaway slave, though I am, of course, a visitor to your fair town and would be appreciative of any hospitality you saw fit to give me.'

While I spoke, every eye in the room had been on me, and after I spoke the eyes remained and several pins came crashing to the floor. Then, as if on signal, there was a thump of glasses hitting wood. 'Let's string him up!' shouted several voices as one. 'Let's get him now!' There was a

76

rumble of what seemed rather like assent.

'I say,' I said, suddenly remembering something I'd heard people say in films that seemed appropriate for the situation, 'I come in peace.'

Someone socked me in the jaw.

In the end, reason prevailed, and they didn't string me up, they pasted me with hot tar, covered me with feathers, and ran me out of town on a rail. 'Don't you ever come back to Venice, Oregon,' they screamed at me.

I never did.

Greed

Humans are obsessed with the macro-world. No matter how many times it is pointed out to them that life is fleeting and transitory, that its essence is non-material, that you can't take your gold chains and BMWs with you when you go, they don't listen. Nowhere else in the universe would you find a creature with only two feet who owned two hundred and ninety-six pairs of shoes. What for? When would you wear them? When would you have time to do anything else *but* wear them? Likewise, it would never occur to any other thing but a man to buy so many teapots, paintings and bits of useless pottery that it had to be stored in a warehouse and never unpacked. In no other galaxy would it be possible for two humanoids and a poodle to own three houses, an apartment, a boat and a private plane. If it were possible, they wouldn't then make the maid pay for any dishes she accidentally broke. And, too, the Lemstocks, Gertrude and Arnie, could only have come from Earth.

Meg Megan, from the planet Tuli

Radaflox, my fellow field astronomer, and I had been up in the hills for several days, charting the northern summer night sky, and so we stopped at the Little Fox Inn for a bit of bread and cheese on the way back. We noticed the couple at the next table the way you would notice people who take twenty minutes to order, but we didn't think anything of it. Not until they ordered their fifth extra-large portion of jumbo shrimps with triple trimmings, did Radaflox turn to me and say, 'Is it my imagination, or did that couple already eat four extra-large portions of jumbo shrimps?'

I said, 'It must be lens distortion, from staring through a fracrascope for five nights solid. They couldn't possibly have eaten all those innocent little crustaceans.'

With a quick glance at the Lemstocks (we learned their names at the inquiry), who were calling for another basket of bread, Radaflox muttered, 'So you saw it too.'

'I'm fatigued,' I said. 'It's physically impossible for anything on this planet smaller than a grizzly to eat that much food. And even then, it would have to be a pretty hungry grizzly. A grizzly who hadn't eaten all winter.'

After the shrimp, Gertrude and Arnie ordered four dozen steamed clams, each, then a bowlful of creamed mashed potatoes, and a large dish of buttered carrots. Radaflox and I, and the other diners sitting near them, had by then abandoned any pretence of eating our own meals, and were staring at the Lemstocks in either awe (if you were human) or horror (if you happened to have arrived from Tuli only a week before). 'Maybe they're built differently or something,' I whispered to Rada. 'You know, maybe it just goes right out through a hole in their feet.'

'Wrong planet,' he whispered back. 'You're thinking of those genetic misfits, the bottomless beasts of Kapoon, doomed never to be satisfied but to spend their lives trying to fill up their emptiness by inhaling everything in sight.'

I watched Gertrude Lemstock shovel half a bowl of carrots into her face and then mop up the sauce with half a loaf of bread. 'Maybe this is Kapoon,' I ventured.

Rada cocked his head and gave it a shake. 'You never hear Mantovani and his orchestra playing 'Blowing in the Wind' in restaurants in Kapoon,' he reminded me. 'And look at the wallpaper.'

I looked at the wallpaper. It was flocked.

'And there's a picture of the Queen over the salad bar.'

There was a picture of the Queen over the salad bar, next to a print of several men on horseback chasing a little fox.

'And the cheese pours and the milk doesn't have to be refrigerated,' said Rada.

'You're right,' I said. 'It's not Kapoon.'

The Lemstocks ordered two dozen more clams and a twelve-egg jam omelette (the specialty of the Little Fox Inn), half a shelf from the cheese trolley and an entire basket of water biscuits. Even at a modest estimate, they had by now eaten enough to give all of Calcutta a feast it wouldn't forget in a long time.

'Maybe they're being put into orbit in deepest space tomorrow and this is their last solid meal for the next ten years,' suggested Rada.

The Lemstocks selected half a chocolate gateau and a bowl of trifle for afters.

I took a sip of water. 'They'd never get off the ground.'

'Maybe they only eat once a year,' said Rada.
'That's possible. You know, it might be
something that developed because of a food
scarcity.'

'Leaping leptons,' I said, 'now they're having
ice-cream.'

'But maybe not,' said Rada. 'If there was a
food scarcity, chances are they caused it.'

Finally, Arnie called for the bill. Gertrude
asked for five doggie-bags.

'I can't stand this,' said Rada. 'I have to ask.'
He pushed his half-eaten toasted cheese sandwich
away and went over to the Lemstocks' table. He
smiled. He nodded. He gestured towards me. The
Lemstocks smiled and nodded. They waved.

'Well?' I asked, when he rejoined me. 'What
did they say?'

'He said his employers gave him and his wife a
free dinner for twenty years of loyal service.'

I said, 'Excuse me?'

Rada shrugged. 'They said there was no limit
to the ticket, that he and his wife should enjoy
themselves.' Our eyes followed the Lemstocks as
they slowly crossed the restaurant, their arms
filled with doggie-bags. Rada sighed. 'So they
did.'

Fun

There isn't a creature in all creation who doesn't like to
have a good time. But few pursue personal pleasure with
the single-mindedness and determination of the human.
Humans love to have fun. If they're having fun, they feel
good; and if they feel good they think that everything must
be all right. The only thing humans spend more time and
money on than having fun is building up their armies.

The question is: Will you, as an alien, be able to recog-

Humans, of course, have a sophisticated concept of fun.

nize human fun when you see it, or will you think it's
something else (a man in only his underwear dancing to
'Devil with the Blue Dress on', with a lampshade over his
head, for example)? In order to help you sharpen your
judgement in this crucial area, the following quiz has been
formulated by our researchers. For each question, select
the best answer from a human point of view.

1. John is getting married on Saturday morning. On Friday night, his friends, Dan, Rick, Mike and Lenny, take him out for a night of fun. They do this because:

   a. they want to celebrate John's good fortune and happiness with him.

   b. marriage is an important rite of passage, signifying as it does the transition from the irresponsible state of youth to that of full manhood and responsibility. As such, it should therefore be appropriately heralded.

   c. once he's married John will never have any fun again.

   d. any excuse is a good one.

2. To mark the occasion of John leaving his childish things behind him and joining the ranks of adult men who have committed themselves to cherishing and protecting one woman and building a life and a family for the two of them, John's friends:

   a. take him to a quiet dinner, during which they reminisce about their boyhoods and toast his future happiness and success.

   b. take him on a nostalgic journey to visit some of their old haunts and places that were the scene of some of John's most cherished memories. They drive past the house where he grew up; they sit in the school playground where they once played ball and whispered about sex; they visit the shop where John first bought clothes without his mother, the shop where he bought his first LP, the barber who first shaved his head, and the newsagent's where they all used to buy the *Beano*. Then, in a symbolic welding of the past and the future, they take John and his bride out to dinner.

    c. take him to a strip club, where John gets very drunk and spends most of the evening trying to stick five pound notes in the dancers' G-strings.

    d. take him to a seedy night-club. While John is trying to beat his own record of twenty-seven seconds for the downing of a pint of bitter, a young woman dressed as a nun comes up to their table, sings a song about John going into the convent, takes off all her clothes, and then pulls down John's trousers. Everyone thinks this is hilariously funny, except John, who, because his trousers are around his ankles, winds up barfing all over the floor.

3.   Linda and April adore Barry Manilow.[24] They think he is a great singer, a great human being, and one of the sexiest men on the face of the Earth. Hearing Barry Manilow sing is their idea of not just ordinary, everyday fun, but of orgasmic happiness. That is why they:

    a. own every album he has ever made.

    b. not only own every album he has ever made, but play them constantly. As Linda says, 'I just have to hear him sing and my blue mood disappears.' As April says, 'The fact that Barry Manilow is on this planet is a source of constant joy to me.'

---

[24] As with many things on Earth, liking Barry Manilow falls into the category of 'personal taste'. Personal taste means that there is no objective or even good reason for liking this thing, you just do. The eminent Yoqian biologist Jala believes that personal taste may be genetic. How else could you explain a fondness for ballroom dancing, hats with veils, or Megadeth?

c. queue up for forty-eight hours in a snowstorm to have Barry Manilow sign his new album for them.

d. join 35,000 people in a football stadium where they all sit on hard benches and stand in spilled beer and pop, too far away from the stage to either see or hear Barry Manilow, assuming, of course, that the slight figure at the piano really is he.

4. To show their undying love, devotion and respect for Barry Manilow, Linda and April:

a. donate money to Barry Manilow's second favourite charity.

b. have a tree planted in his name.

c. name their cats Barry and Manilow respectively.

d. paper their rooms in pictures of Barry Manilow and sleep on sheets and pillowcases on which his profile has been tastefully reproduced in sepia.

5. Recently, a survey of several thousand ordinary people was conducted to find out what they enjoyed doing most in their free time. The majority:

a. selected spending time with their families.

b. selected helping others.

c. selected shopping.

d. didn't know.

6. Brittany and Lloyd have been saving for the past ten years to take one wonderful, unforgettable, dream-

fulfilling holiday together. They have skimped, they have scrimped, and they have gone without Saturdays at the pubs and Sunday lunches at the carvery in the local hotel — all in anticipation of this, the holiday of a lifetime. 'Fun,' Lloyd says to Brittany, 'darling, we are going to redefine the word.' How do Lloyd and Brittany redefine the word 'fun'?

a. They build a boat in which they sail around the world for two years of non-stop romance and adventure.

b. They backpack through the Himalayas. They visit Tibet. They ride camels in Nepal and elephants in India. They sail the China Sea in a junk. They make love on the moon-silvered shores of Bali. Together they count the stars over Thailand. At the end of their twenty-eight-month journey, they return to Bognor Regis with a new sense of peace, harmony and unspeakable joy.

c. They go to Hawaii. They stay in the best hotel and drink a lot of cocktails with funny names, all of which are served in coconut shells and topped with paper parasols. Brittany brings home three dozen plastic leis as souvenirs for her friends, and Lloyd takes 3,600 photographs of their holiday, only thirty-six of which aren't overexposed (those are the thirty-six that were taken of Brittany and Lloyd, wearing their Hawaiian shirts and paper leis, by strangers).

d. They take a package tour to Europe. Along with one hundred and fifty other intrepid tourists sporting cameras, straw hats and name tags, they spend fourteen days in a bus and thirteen nights in small hotel rooms, all of which look the same. When they return home, Charley next door asks them if they went to Seville. Lloyd gets out the itinerary to check.

7. Stu and Ellen go to Dick's and Suzette's for dinner. After dinner, Dick suggests a game of Trivial Pursuit. 'Oh, that'll be fun,' agree the others. 'We love board games.' Stu, Ellen, Dick and Suzette play Trivial Pursuit. They:

a. enjoy themselves.

b. learn a lot about world geography, horse racing and 1960's television shows in the process. Everyone is amazed at Stu's extensive knowledge of Japanese cinema, Ellen's grasp of the physical sciences, Dick's familiarity with British literature, and how many historical battles Suzette has committed to memory.

c. have an argument over the exact year in which *The Catcher in the Rye* was first published and the exact location of Japan. As a result of this argument, Stu and Ellen go home early, and Suzette, convinced that it was all Dick's fault, makes him sleep on the couch.

d. come to blows when Suzette refuses to play any more because of Dick's patronizing attitude, and Stu, agitated because Ellen lost them a wedge because she always confuses Orson Welles with George Orwell, calls her an idiot. As a result of this fight, Ellen leaves Stu for a man with the reading level of a ten-year-old, and Suzette throws the Trivial Pursuit into the waste disposal. It costs two hundred and fifty pounds to repair the disposal.

8. The lads (all of whom are over twenty) are going to see their favourite team play a bunch of Italians. As their wives and sweethearts say, 'They're football mad.' Nothing makes them happier than a game, unless it's two games. They have been looking forward to this for weeks. For days before they talk of nothing else. The big day dawns. Off they go. They:

a. enjoy the game.

b. later liken seeing Monihan score a goal right through the legs of the opposition's goalie to a spiritual experience.

c. drink so much beer before they go that they fall asleep half-way through.

d. meet a group of Italy supporters on the train on the way to the game. One of the Italians is overheard to say to his friends, 'Remember the last time these teams played each other? We wiped the stadium with them.' This so insults the lads that they have no recourse but to express their feelings in a way that can't be misunderstood. As a result of this brawl, they spend the afternoon in jail and miss the game completely.

9.   While the lads are at their game — or supposedly at their game — the girls go off for some fun of their own. They:

a. go out for lunch and a film.

b. go out for lunch and a poetry reading.

c. go shopping.

d. go shopping, have their hair done, and then do some more shopping.

10.   Mr Brown has been looking forward to his holiday all year long. All year long, he works five days a week at a job that manages to be both extremely complicated and demanding and mind-bogglingly boring. Not only that, but he commutes to work by car, a journey that takes an hour and a half each way when traffic is moving, and

three when it isn't. It usually isn't. It would, in fact, be fair to say that Mr Brown doesn't just look forward to his yearly holiday; he lives for it. This year for his holiday, Mr Brown is taking Mrs Brown and the three little Browns:

a. absolutely nowhere. They are going to stay home and relax. Mr Brown is going to catch up on his reading. Mrs Brown is going to finish the loft. The little Browns are going to be able to spend quality time with their father, instead of only seeing him when he is tired, grumpy and wants nothing more than to lie on the couch with a cold cloth over his eyes and a gin-and-tonic drip. Mr Brown and Mrs Brown are going to stay up past eleven and make love in the garden by the light of the moon.

b. nowhere. The little Browns are being hustled off to their grandparents for two weeks, and Mr Brown and Mrs Brown are having a second honeymoon. They are going to stay in a first-class hotel. They are going to have room service. They are going to fritter their days away by the pool. Mr Brown is going to teach Mrs Brown how to play snooker, just like he did on their first honeymoon. Mrs Brown is going to beat Mr Brown at snooker again. They are going to laugh and sing and recapture their youths, and return to their daily lives refreshed and invigorated.

c. camping. Mrs Brown thinks that there is less chance of the children ruining their holiday completely if they aren't kept in an enclosed space. Mr Brown tells everybody that he's really looking forward to getting in touch with nature. As someone who works in an office, he tells everyone, it's important to get out into the real world of trees, dirt and slime beetles every so often. Mrs Brown turns out to have been wrong about Northumberland being so large that her children couldn't possibly give her a two-week migraine if let loose in it; and Mr Brown fails to take into account the fact that he and nature have never really cared for one another that much. Especially considering how he feels about spiders.

d. to a world-famous theme park for two weeks. This theme park is so big that it takes two weeks to really see it — not to mention spend so much money that the Browns will never be able to go on holiday again. The highlight of the trip is when the entire family has its picture taken with Goofy.

11. Ed has the sudden realization one day that his life is dull and empty. 'What do I do?' Ed asks himself. And then he answers himself. 'I go to work, I come home. I eat dinner. I watch TV. I go to bed. I get up. I go to work. I come home. Etc.' Ed gets depressed. 'But there must be more to life than this,' he says. 'Where are the excitement and adventure? Where is the fun?' Where does Ed decide the excitement, adventure, and fun are?

a. In art, literature and music. He begins to read more, to visit museums and attend concerts. Then he starts to write a little himself. He takes oboe lessons. He gets himself a set of water colours. He becomes a new man. Instead of sleep-walking through his life, he now stops and looks at every day and every thing. Just a sunset can delight him. Just a passing conversation amuse or move him. Ed realizes that there are no dull lives, just dull people.

b. In science. He becomes fascinated with biology and botany. There are universes of wonder in the tiniest toad or the smallest petal. He begins to think about how things work and why. He begins to question all the things he has always taken for granted: birth, death, grass, trees, stars, the sun, that funny old moon. Ed becomes a new man. A man to whom nothing is uninteresting or beneath his notice or curiosity.

c. In exercise. Ed buys satin running shorts, a terry-cloth sweatband and an expensive pair of running shoes that have a speedometer and a tellurometer embedded in the toes. Ed becomes a new man. His calves harden. He sweats a lot. He suffers a mild heart attack. The heart attack makes him realize how much he prefers life to death, even if it is a dull life.

d. In partying. Ed starts going out all the time. He goes to every party he's invited to. He sprints off to the pub right after dinner. He invites his friends round to celebrate anything and everything from Groundhog Day to the day his car passes its MOT. Ed's having the time of his life. Of course, he doesn't actually remember much — if any — of the time his life is having, but he knows he must be having fun because he always has a hangover and he spends a lot of time communicating with the loo.

12. Rasputin Elder is one of the most famous news photographers on the planet. Rasputin is always winning awards. He has got where he is, he says, because he loves his work. He absolutely loves it. But of all the thousands of interesting, exciting and fun-filled assignments that Rasputin has had, the one he enjoyed most was:

a. the photo essay he did on Mother Theresa.

b. photographing gorillas in Africa.

c. photographing the war in Nicaragua.

d. photographing the war in Vietnam. He liked Vietnam better than Nicaragua, because he was wounded in Vietnam but managed to come out of Nicaragua unscathed. Rasputin says there's nothing as exciting as a war, especially if you nearly die. It makes you feel so alive.

How did you score? Do you understand what humans consider having a good time, or are you still handicapped by the alien concept that personal enjoyment should combine utility and feeling as well as cheap thrills? Give yourself one (1) point for every a. you answered; two (2) for every b; three (3) for every c; and four (4) for every d. If you achieved a score of between twelve (12) and twenty-four (24), you've been watching too many situation comedies. Even though your answers are based on what can be seen as human logic, they don't take that important extra step from the ideal to the real. If you scored between thirty (30) and thirty-six (36), you are beginning to understand the human being and to appreciate the subtlety of its heart and mind. Similarly, a score of between thirty-seven (37) and forty-two (42) suggests that you have become something of an expert when it comes to the field of human behaviour. If, however, you scored between forty-three (43) and forty-eight (48), you may be in need of what the Americans used to call R & R (Rest and Relaxation). For the Americans R & R meant two weeks drinking, whoring and taking drugs. For you, a few days in a cave with a Buddhist monk should do the trick.

Aggression

Humans like to joke among themselves that there are a few of them on the planet who are still naturally aggressive. Short people, for example, are thought to be aggressive. People from cold climates. Bus drivers, tax inspectors, old women in queues, mercenaries, corporate executives, football fans, disadvantaged youths, the managers of launderettes and small grocery stores, waiters, and so forth. But they say it, of course, as a joke.

For humans believe that force, violence, and mindless pushiness are as anachronistic to their way of being as the slingshot or the spear. As members of what they see to be an advanced civilization, they feel that they have learned to control their more primitive emotions and drives. They are, they believe, no longer the victims of their fears and instincts. It is almost the year 2,000, after all. They don't belong to Attila's Huns. They have therapists, support groups, self-help books and rebirthing clinics. Casual rape, pillage and naked aggression are no longer encouraged.

But humans are wrong about this, too.

Anyone who has ever gone Christmas shopping knows that any Hun who suddenly found himself on a twentieth-century street on the 24th of December would be begging to go back to the invasion of Europe inside an hour.

The lights are twinkling, the carollers are carolling, the air is filled with the aroma of roasting chestnuts, and the shops are filled with signs advertizing peace and goodwill.

Our unsuspecting barbarian, his necklace made of human bone bits rattling in the seasonal wind, starts marching down the street. Smeared with dirt, blood and sheep grease as he is, he looks pretty fierce and intimidating, for a primitive Hun. But not half as fierce and intimidating as the last-minute shoppers who surround him. Collars turned up, hats pulled down, bulging carrier-bags grasped to their bodies like Mudukian shields, they swarm across the pavement, their faces grim with determination, their eyes hard and empty. They care not for the weak, the elderly, or the very young. They look neither left nor right, but plough on, trampling everyone and everything underfoot. Normally, of course, this sort of behaviour would make our barbarian feel right at home. But not now. Now it seems a little frightening and distressing. He wishes his pet wolf or his mother were with him. As he tries, largely unsuccessfully, to shoulder his way through the crowd, our Hun looks at the faces around, and all at once realizes what is wrong. These people aren't fighting for survival in vicious and turbulent times. These people aren't changing the history of Europe. These people are shopping!

'Stone me,' mutters our barbarian, an unwise thing to say too loudly. 'I'm glad Attila's not here to see this. Killer grannies and cold-blooded housewives. It would destroy his self-confidence once and for all.'

He's right to be nervous.

Within the first five minutes (the amount of time it takes him to travel the three yards to the corner) his club, knife and flint are lifted by a pickpocket dressed as Santa Claus. He only just avoids being embroiled in a rather vicious fight between two shoppers trying to get into the same taxi by allowing himself to be walked over by a group of young men who are drinking beer and singing 'Jingle Bells'.

He has sacked a few towns in his career, our barbarian, so he's no stranger to mob mentality, but, nevertheless, by the time he does reach the corner, he is visibly shaken. Not only are there footprints on his back and a ringing in his ears from the punch he took because he got too close to the would-be cab riders, but he has been pushed off the kerb twice, shoved into a lamp-post four times, had his heel stepped on at least thirteen times, his toes bruised, and been smacked in the head by no less than six rolls of festive wrapping paper. In addition, he has been called some names that would have made Attila blush. Being part of an invading horde, and not part of a highly-evolved culture, our barbarian does not apologize for being pushed, shoved, stepped on and clobbered, as many humans would, but growls. He rattles his bones. He would wave his knife, but that's been nicked, so he shakes his fist instead. A woman with a pushchair knocks him over. Her child hurls a juice bottle at him. Our barbarian staggers to his feet in order to assess the damage. Three people, all of whom have their eyes open, immediately walk into him.

He decides to head for cover.

Still growling, though a trifle more softly, he tries

storming into the first major department store he comes to. Storming citadels isn't what it used to be. He has to make four separate attempts to enter. The first time he is pushed back by gimlet-eyed shoppers coming out. The second, the door is slammed in his face by a sweet-looking old lady. The third time he is thrown back by a laughing gaggle of teenagers. The fourth time, he goes straight through the glass. No one notices. Several people follow him through. Not until he finds himself ground to a halt in a herd of shoppers and pinioned against a display of humorous boxer shorts do the prophetic words of that old Hun saying come to his mind: off of the spit and into the pit.

Our barbarian is beginning to know not why the caged bird sings, but why it beats its wings against the bars. Claustrophobia is something of a new concept to someone from the second century BC, as it is to those of us from deepest space, but he catches on to it pretty quickly. The crowd decides to move from humorous boxer shorts to housewares. Our barbarian — having, indeed, no choice in the matter — moves with them. Unaccustomed to escalators, he gets a bit of his boot caught in the mechanism, and can't get off when it is his turn to disembark. Not to worry, though. No one notices this either. Fifty-eight shoppers stampede over his prostrate form. It is about then that our Hun longs to be facing someone with a bloody spear and a desire to destroy civilization.

Ego

Ego is what makes it possible for Man, one of the more insignificant life-forms in the universe, to think that he is so important that not only does God care what he does,[25] but everyone else in the cosmos cares as well.

Megoyd, of the planet Q8

After my experience in Venice, Oregon, I had
rather a hankering to return to the meteorite
showers and Metax Field aberrations of Q8. I had
no desire to go to Oxford Street, baseball cap or
no baseball cap, and I was wary of venturing
anywhere else on the planet, in any time.
Considering my experiences of the nineteenth
and twentieth centuries to date, I certainly didn't
want to risk getting caught up in the Dark Ages,
one of the Crusades, or the Holocaust. But I had
a mission to finish, so, of course, the choice was
not really mine to make. My personal transporter
was still acting up, though, so no sooner had I
pulled the last few feathers from my shorts, than I
was sitting on a bus next to Mrs Miller. Mrs

---

[25] It never occurs to Man that God gave up on him a long time
ago. And who can blame Him? God gave Man commandments,
and Man immediately ripped them to shreds. Having been told
not to kill, he then proceeded to kill in the name of God. Having
been advised against worshipping false gods, he moved from
worshipping money, power and nationalism to worshipping
movie stars, rock'n'roll singers and psychoanalysts. Having been
told to honour his father and his mother, he invented the Sunny
Brook Retirement Home. Having been entrusted with the care
and maintenance of a rather pretty little planet and some very
attractive lower life-forms, he immediately set about destroying
them all. He made rugs out of the larger furry mammals, umbrella
stands out of the feet of elephants and trinkets out of their tusks,
he boiled down the whale, levelled mountains, paved over the
forests, polluted the oceans, turned the blue sky yellow and
created that legendary tellurian phenomenon, the burning river.
Given an enviable bounty of fruits and vegetables, he came up
with cheese in a tin. In fact, it could be said that the only evidence
Man has that God has had any interest in him in the last 2,000
years or so was Jesus Christ, and him they nailed to a cross.

Miller immediately began to tell me her life story. It was fairly routine, until 1989, when Mrs Miller was visited by small, silver creatures with big heads, large eyes and slender, delicate hands, who landed their spacecraft in her back garden, doing damage to several beds of geraniums.

I've travelled through quite a few galaxies in my time, but I'd never run into anything that fitted Mrs Miller's description. Not to mention that the craft she described sounded a little old-fashioned as well. 'How fascinating,' I said. 'What planet did they come from?'

'Oh, I've never been very good at names,' said Mrs Miller, 'but I think it started with a P or maybe it was an X.'

I nodded thoughtfully. 'I see,' I said. 'A P or an X. And why did they say they'd come?'

'Oh, to warn us,' said Mrs Miller, matter-of-factly, as though I should have known that.

'Warn us?' I asked, trying to keep from sounding too surprised. 'Warn us of what?'

'That we're destroying the planet,' explained Mrs Miller. 'That was their message. That if we don't stop dumping toxic wastes in our seas, razing the rain forests, and wiping out whole species there'll soon be nothing left.'

'They crossed time and space, traversing the universe and risking unknown horrors and disasters to tell us that?'

Mrs Miller nodded her head. 'That's right.'

I knew I should get her back on to the topic of her neighbour with the ten cats, but I couldn't let it be. 'You don't think that's a little strange?' I ventured.

'Strange?' asked Mrs Miller, peering back at me as though *I* were strange. 'What's strange about that?'

'Well,' I said, 'it's a long way to come to tell us something we already know.'

'They care about us,' said Mrs Miller simply.

The unasked — and in Mrs Miller's case, unthought — question hovered in the air above us. *But why?*

'But why?' I wanted to shout at her. 'Why should beings from another solar system care about Man? Do you think they're desperate for McDonald's? Do you think they feel their lives are incomplete because they don't have Ninja Turtle cereal and day-glo sun-glasses?'

I wanted to say to her, 'Look, missus, you people are already throwing your garbage into space. Do you think there's an advanced life-form in the universe that doesn't know that, given half a chance, you'll have billboards

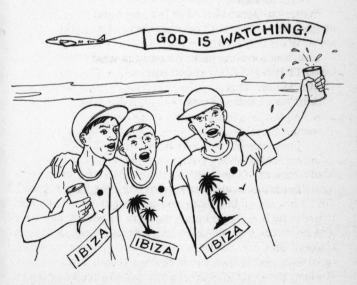

Other life-forms envy Man his spirit and imagination.

97

advertizing soft drinks and automobiles orbitting the sun? That you'll have fast food chains up and down the Milky Way? That you'll colonize Minata and C22 just the way you colonized Africa and North America: here's five pounds, whisky, and a dose of smallpox, just let us have the mineral rights?'

'They *do*?' I managed to gasp.

Mrs Miller was nodding her head again. 'Yes,' she was saying, 'they do.' She folded up her knitting. 'The thing is,' said Mrs Miller, 'that for all their technology and special powers, I think they rather envy us.'

Outside the window, several loud young men in baseball caps with pin-wheels on the top and T-shirts with the silhouette of a palm tree and the word 'Ibiza' on the front staggered by.

'Envy us?' said I.

'Yes,' said Mrs Miller. 'For our spirit and imagination. They don't have anything like it, you know.'

Overhead, a plane pulling a sign that said GOD IS WATCHING glided past.

She had me there.

'Oh, yes,' I said. 'I know.'

Fear

Many eminent behaviourists, sociologists and anthropologists believe that the primary force driving Man is greed. Give him one potato crisp and he'll want two. Give him two and he'll grab the entire bag. Try to get the bag back and he'll deck you and call it self-defence. 'Look at human history,' they say. 'There has been no event, great or small, ignoble or saintly, that someone hasn't made a profit on it. And as though it isn't bad enough that avarice has marked every human relationship since Adam and Eve decided that the pears, the plums, the oranges, the kumquats and the mangoes weren't sufficient, they had to have the apples, too, it has marked his relationship with everything else on the planet as well. Only Man would befriend you, feed you and bring you in by the fire, and then pour soap in your eyes and give you cancer.'

True, all true. But nonetheless, no matter how it seems on the surface, it isn't really greed that has determined the course of Man's history.

'No?'

No.

'What is it then?'

It is fear.

Every creature in the universe, of course, is afraid of something. Some are afraid of black holes. Some are afraid of infinity. Some don't like to get wet or have to touch Urgons. Most get a little nervous when a two-ton Pp launches itself at their head. Hunger, pain, being stuck in a convention of accountants at Chelmsford, or forced to attend a night of Wagner performed by the primary school of East Ealing, all of these are things likely to strike terror in the hardest of hearts, but Man's fear is simpler.

Man is afraid of everything. He is afraid of everything — from putting on too much weight to going bald and getting old — but mostly he is afraid of being alone.

It is because of his fear of being alone that Man is always trying to get other animals — cats, dogs, birds, ferrets, boa constrictors, etc. — to move in with and be like him. He gives them names like Patsy, Bob and Rufus Blue the III. He teaches them to talk, and if they can't talk, he talks for them.

'Does Rufus Blue the III want a little piece of cheese?' he asks. Rufus Blue, one of the fattest and laziest beagles the cosmos has ever seen, looks at him without raising his head. He wheezes. 'Yes, Dad,' says Man, in the squeaky baby voice he somehow imagines belongs to Rufus Blue (who is not only fat and lazy but mean as well). 'Yes, I would love a piece of cheese. Make it big.'

Man loves his pets.

He makes them wear boots and raincoats and track-suits. He puts foam reindeer antlers and Santa Claus hats on them at Christmas. He lets them eat off his plate and sleep in his bed. He invents diet dog food and gourmet cat food. He teaches his dog to carry his own lead when they walk down the street, and his cat to open the refrigerator. 'Look,' he says, 'look at the way Hanky Poo watches television. Don't you think she's almost human?'

But no other animal on the planet is almost human. Bears don't decimate the forests. Raccoons don't make coats out of chinchillas. Zebras don't enslave other zebras. Dogs don't drive cars. Lions don't make pets out of fruit bats. Hamsters don't build fast food chains. Cats don't sell arms to the death squads in Guatemala.

But these details don't bother Man. Man will happily anthropomorphize anything from a rat to a strawberry poison-dart frog, all because he can't bear to think that he is all alone on this tiny planet, spinning through space, the only creature capable of asking (or with any interest in asking) the one question to which there is no answer.[26]

---

[26] This one question is: What am I doing here?

It is because of his fear of being alone that advertizing is such an important part of tellurian life. Advertizing can only work among creatures who want to belong, to fit in, to have the approval of the world at large. Beings who are content to go their own way, to smell their own smell, to have a white phone when everyone else has a blue one, or wear gym shoes when everyone else is wearing trainers with neon laces aren't going to be incapable of buying so much as a tube of toothpaste unless they're sure it's the brand that everyone else uses.

It is also because of his fear of being alone that Man is so addicted to noise. Silence drives him crazy. He can think when it's silent, or perform the human equivalent: analyzing his relationship with his mother and worrying that he's ill/going bald/needs a new car/will never get promoted/is putting on weight. And once that begins, of course, one worry leads to another. He starts by wondering if that bruise on his knee is not the result of bumping into the wall while trying to slam dance after all, but symptomatic of something chronic, and he ends by wondering how much God is really going to hold against him. Death camps? Slavery? War? The CIA? The dolphins? Filching paper clips and typewriter ribbons from the office?

Thus Man came up with noisy cities. Noisy clubs. Noisy pubs. Television. Radio. The personal stereo and the ghetto blaster. Musak. Who could worry about the meaning of death while forty violins and a cello are playing 'Raindrops Keep Falling on My Head'?

And, of course, it is also because of his fear of being alone that Man believes in extraterrestrial invasions. It makes him feel less uneasy about his ride through space and the fact that he has no idea what he is doing to believe that he is so important that other beings might want to take over his cities or warn him about the adverse effects of air pollution.

More Fear

Accompanying the fear of being alone, much as death accompanied the bubonic plague, is the fear of being forgotten. This is the other prime force behind human behaviour, the force that, grunting and groaning, pushes Man along. Man has expended so much energy convincing himself of his own importance, because, deep down, he is terrified that the opposite is true: that he is so unimportant that the minute he goes out of sight he is forgotten. 'Man?' the other animals say to one another as night descends and they are left in peace for a while. 'Who's that?'

And, of course, Man especially doesn't want God to forget who he is. Then he'd really be alone. From the most primitive human — sacrificing small animals and offering the sun bowls of corn — to the most sophisticated — bombing planes and department stores and levelling cities — Man has constantly tried to catch God's attention. 'I'm here!' he keeps screaming. 'Right here, between Venus and Mars. You remember me, don't you? You've noticed how much I do for you, haven't you?' He convinces himself every time there's a good yearly rainfall that God isn't peering over the clouds and saying, 'Who?'

Sex

Sex is another of those things that Man has missed the point of.

On the Earth, sex is a routine biological function, necessary for the preservation and continuation of life. But the creator understood what he was up against. Something this vital and important couldn't be left to human control.

Imagine, for instance, what would have happened if sex was not only less pleasurable than eating cheese on toast, but optional as well ... Eons have passed. The human species is dying out. No one can be bothered to bother.

Later, they promise. Tomorrow. I'm too busy right now. A man and a woman — two of the few survivors — are sitting around one evening, looking at the moon and a million stars like fireflies.

'What shall we do now?' asks the woman.

The man shrugs. 'Don't know,' he says. 'We could go hang gliding, or night hunting, or white water rafting, I suppose.'

'Those are all a bit dangerous,' says the woman. She stretches beside him.

'But they're fun,' the man protests.

She looks a little coy, leaning her head against his shoulder. 'What else could we do?'

He gives it some thought. 'Well, I guess we could drink so much whisky that we throw up,' he says at last. 'I always like that a lot.'

The woman slides over a little closer. 'But drinking's bad for you,' she whispers. 'There must be something else we could do. Something sort of pleasant.'

'Drugs?' suggests the man.

'Oh, not drugs,' says the woman. 'Drugs are as bad as alcohol. They turn you into a soft potato who tells the same story over and over. What can we do that's good exercise and potentially beneficial to the species as a whole?'

'You want to go to another part of town and beat up people who are different to us?'

She rolls her eyes and sighs in exasperation. 'What I was thinking of was sex,' says the woman.

He turns to her warily. 'Sex?' he repeats.

'You know,' she coaxes. 'Kissing and hugging. The positive use of energy for the expression of affection and for possible procreation. Sex.'

He frowns. 'But sex isn't fun,' he argues. 'You have to get undressed, and you get all sweaty, and sometimes it takes hours before anything happens. I mean, it's all right, and I know it has its place, but couldn't we just watch TV instead?'

103

So, to avoid such situations, the creator made sex extremely enjoyable. Enjoyable and simple. Simple enough for the simplest human male to be capable of doing it, and enjoyable enough that he would want to. And that's where the hitch comes in.

Since sex is so enjoyable, Man carries on not as though it's a routine biological function shared by aardvarks and *Homo sapiens* alike, but as though he invented it. Not only does he carry on as though he invented it, he maintains a rather awesome ambiguity about this invention. Is it one of his better achievements, or one of his worst? Is it a pleasant physical experience, a meaningful form of emotional communication, or more evil than the bombing of Cambodia? Half of mankind acts as though sex was invented to give people something *really* depraved and nasty to do; and the other half acts as though Man invented it because, though God tried His best, life itself just wasn't up to much without it.

No matter what your point of view, though, the basic fact is that Man relates to sex differently than any other species that has ever existed.

Everyone else just does it.

The suns are sinking over the silver mesas of Lqu. The air is humming. The mud swamps are bubbling. A delicious tingle runs up your spine. You turn to the being beside you, and you say, 'Hey, I've got a good idea. Let's have sex.' And so you do.

But not Man. Man has to think about it first. He thinks about it, and then he feels guilty for thinking about it. Then he thinks about it some more. Then he talks about it. Man talks about sex all the time. He worries that, as a child, he saw his father naked. He worries that he didn't see his father naked. He wonders if he'd feel better adjusted about sex if he had ever caught his parents in The Act. He spends fifteen years and a small fortune in therapy, because he was traumatized by once seeing his parents in bed together. If he believes that sex is a good thing, then he can never get enough of it. He'll have sex

104

with anyone and everyone, even a rubber doll or his best friend's mate, and then he'll call it love. He'll use sex to prove that he is attractive, alive, worthwhile, interesting, and will never die. If, on the other hand, he thinks sex is sinful, having sex once, fully dressed, in a closet with the lights out and a bag over his head, will have been too much.

Edna Vz, from the planet Avo

The one thing I was really looking forward to on Earth, besides the artichoke pizza and wind surfing, was sex. You know, it seemed like it would be fun. They talk about it so much, and they have all these books and magazines and films and articles and shows and ads about it, and they're always making jokes about it, or using it to sell toothpaste and cars ... so it seemed like it must be pretty interesting, right? Wrong. I figured they knew what they were doing. And then I met Damian Pinelli.

Damian Pinelli was, in his words, a man of the world. 'I've been around, baby,' is how he phrased it, though he had never been outside the Earth's atmosphere. He was handsome in a male human sort of way. You know, not someone you'd want to be Commander of the Intergalactic Federation or anything, but nice to slow dance with and handy when you couldn't get the lid off the pickles. We dated for a few months, and then things started getting serious. One night, when we were being particularly romantic, Damian turned to me and said, 'Look, Edna. Just look at that hand.'

I looked. It had five digits, blunt-cut nails, and a small scar on the back where his brother had stabbed him with a screwdriver when they were kids. 'Yes?' I said. 'What about it?'

'Look at the size of it.' He held it up. 'Don't you know what that means?' He grinned.

'That you should go into construction?'

He winked. 'It means that you're a lucky, lucky girl,' he whispered. He winked again. 'A very lucky girl.' He stuck his tongue in my ear.

'Lucky?' I repeated. 'Honey, what do you mean?'

He pinched my bum. 'I mean big,' he cooed. 'Big like a truncheon.'

I looked at him curiously. 'What's big like a truncheon?' I wanted to know.

'My rabbit, Peter,' said Damian.

I began to get the drift. 'Oh, *him*,' I exclaimed. Damian didn't mean that he owned a giant rabbit named Peter. Peter the rabbit was what he called his penis, though I never managed to find out why. It just didn't seem like the sort of thing you could ask someone straight out. 'Wait a minute,' I said, 'didn't I read somewhere that the size of a man's penis has no bearing on his sexual performance? Isn't it more a question of sensitivity and sensuality? Of passion and finesse?'

Damian waved his enormous hand in a scoffing manner. 'The bloke who wrote that has a dick the size of a slug.' He wrapped his fist around my fingers. 'Believe me, baby, it's just the same as with cars and bikes. Big is better.'

We went back to his place.

Because I had never enjoyed (or not enjoyed) physical intimacy with a man before, Damian was especially helpful, kind and patient. He gave me a black lace suspender belt and a peek-a-boo bra to wear. He told me to bounce up and down on the bed, while he sat on the floor, drinking a beer. I was just getting a little tired of bouncing up and down like the gravity had gone, when Damian

106

took out his penis. It wasn't that big. That is, it was big for a human, but it was small string beans if you came from Avo.

'Isn't it beautiful?' he asked in a deep, husky voice.

That was when I made my second mistake. 'It looks like it's still evolving,' I said. Fortunately, I was laughing, so he thought I was kidding.

'We'll see about that,' he cried, forgetting as he lunged for me that his shorts were around his ankles.

I helped him up.

Foreplay took five minutes. It wouldn't have taken that long, but he insisted on removing my bra and suspender belt with his teeth, a skill he'd acquired through a magazine.

When it was all over, he asked me if the Earth had moved for me too.

I said, 'Of course it moved,' meaning that the Earth is always moving; it would have been much more remarkable if our coming together had made it stop.

I guess it was the right thing to say, though, because he lit a cigarette, sat back, and began to tell me his life story.

Religion

There is more to Man than meets the eye. There'd almost have to be, of course, but it will nonetheless come as something of a relief to many an intergalactic traveller to learn that there is. Man is not just game shows, soap operas and televised war. He is not just a pint of beer, a bag of chips and loud music. Sure, he likes to make a few quid and salt it away. Sure, he likes to exercise his penis whenever he gets the chance. Of course he's not going to say no to a Jaguar or three weeks in the Bahamas or a five-thousand-pound sofa. But you make a mistake if you think that money, sex, fast cars and material goods are his only interests in life.

Religion is what Man is really about. Religion is Man's essence and his soul. Through it he can express the inexpressible, reaffirm his connection with the beauty and the power of the universe, and rise above the problems and uncertainties of life, and the childish differences that separate him from his sisters and brothers. Worrying about work, or not having a date for Saturday night, or his cholesterol level makes Man small and petty; but religion makes him larger than he is. Religion allows Man to cast away the limitations and blindness of a temporal society and shout into the infinite: 'I am one with the suns and the moons and the stars! I have always been and shall always be!'

We are, of course, speaking theoretically here.

Sessia Murutu Q, from Satellite 252

Two or three hundred years ago, my grandfather, then in charge of a 5,000-strong intergalactic force responsible for the safety and well-being of twenty-four different planets, used to spend his holidays on the Earth. When there, he always stayed on a remote sub-tropical island that was inhabited by a tribe of small, dark people who called themselves the Only Ones. The Only Ones led a simple existence. They hunted, fished, ate fruit and cultivated a few root vegetables. Three times a day, they left out offerings of food and flowers to their gods in beautiful little woven baskets. Once a month, at the full moon, they celebrated life and gave thanks for it by singing and dancing beneath the stars. They were a peaceful people, who, not having to struggle to survive, spent a great deal of their time making beautiful things out of driftwood and shells and composing happy songs.

Like the Only Ones themselves, my grandfather believed that they were just that. He had no idea, as he said, that only a few feet away, as it were, there were other humans of a less equable temperament.

And then, one otherwise ordinary, quiet day, while my grandfather and the Only Ones were relaxing on the beach, making tiny stars and moons out of abalone, they spotted three ships coming their way.

'What do you think that is?' asked the Only Ones.

My grandfather shrugged. 'Beats me,' he said.

Which would turn out not to be far from the truth.

The three ships, as the Only Ones and my grandfather soon discovered, were under the command of Captain Alphons Hanolon and manned by an international crew of criminals, losers, psychopaths, and opportunists, working for the good of the King and the glory of God. Captain Hanolon immediately claimed the Only Ones' island in the name of Spain, his crew immediately started attacking the men and raping the women, and Father Sebastian, the company's priest and spiritual advisor, immediately set about teaching them religion.

The first thing Father Sebastian taught them, was that they were riddled with sin. He put them in clothes, stopped them from singing and laughing all the time, forbade them their offerings to the sun and the moon, and taught them the Ten Commandments. My grandfather pointed out that the Ten Commandments had no real relevancy to the Only Ones, since they didn't even have any words in their language for lying, stealing, killing or adultery, never mind the deeds themselves.

'Do you want them all to go to hell?' asked Father Sebastian.

'But hell didn't exist for these people until you came along,' reasoned my grandfather. 'They don't even know what evil is.'

'That just shows you how damned they are,' said Father Sebastian.

Captain Hanolon jailed my grandfather as a heretic. 'Look at him,' said Captain Hanolon. 'He isn't a native. I knew he was a Jew the minute I clapped eyes on him.' He frowned in thought. 'I just can't figure out how he got here.'

Father Sebastian shook his head sadly. 'The legions of the Devil are everywhere,' he said.

For the first time in hundreds — if not thousands — of years, a division formed among the Only Ones, between those who believed in Father Sebastian's God, and those who believed in the god of the sun and the god of the moon. To prove that it was right, each side began killing off members of the other. My grandfather, unaccustomed to such hatred and division, and troubled by the destruction of the tranquil world of the Only Ones, escaped from his leg irons and became the leader of the rebels.

Then three more ships arrived, under the command of Captain Donal Spur. Captain Spur claimed the island in the name of the British King, his international crew of cutthroats, sociopaths, victims and derelicts began warring with Captain Hanolon's (when they weren't killing or raping Only Ones), and the Reverend Murgatroyd and his sister, Alicia, started straightening everyone out on which religion the One True God belonged to. When my grandfather, under a truce flag, went to explain to Captain Spur that everything would be fine on the island if only he and Captain Hanolon took their men, their missionaries and their ships and went somewhere else, Captain Spur had him thrown into jail for heresy and insurrection.

My grandfather returned to his own command after smallpox wiped out almost the entire Only Ones population.

The first time I myself went to Earth, I went to visit my grandfather's island. It had been turned into a resort. There was nude bathing on the beaches, gambling in the casino, and porn films on the cable TV. The few descendants of the Only Ones performed native dances around the main swimming pool on Thursday, Friday and Saturday nights.

Hypocrisy

The only two labour-saving devices created by humans that have ever really worked are slavery — which was not only efficient but didn't harm the environment — and hypocrisy — without which nothing would work at all.

Hypocrisy allows a person to say one thing, believing in it fervently of course, while doing the direct opposite, thus keeping the wheels of society greased and turning. Hypocrisy allows governments to talk about freedom and human rights while destroying them, big businesses to talk about the good of the consumer while putting toxins in their products, and Mr F to tell Mrs F how much he loves her while fooling around with his secretary.

Human Nature: The Quiz

Select the answer which best fits. It is possible that for some questions more than one answer might be correct; we want the one that best typifies what you believe to be human nature.

1. A and B are close friends. One day, A has to go to Barcelona for a week, and asks B to stay in his flat and look after his plants and his iguana while he's away. The first thing A does after B has left is:

    a. water the plants and feed the iguana.

    b. call everyone he knows on A's telephone.

    c. go through all of A's things.

2. The one request A has made of B is not to touch the washing-machine, because it's been acting up lately and may flood, which tends to upset the people downstairs. B:

    a. doesn't touch the washing-machine.

    b. decides that A meant that he shouldn't use the washing-machine for anything heavy, but that a light load is fine, floods A's flat, and loosens half the ceiling of the people downstairs.

    c. decides to do A a favour and fix the washing-machine. Sadly, when B is putting all the bits back, there is one bit that doesn't fit. B throws it away. It takes him so long to repair the machine that he never uses it. He also doesn't tell A that he's fixed it, or that it had one washer too many. Thus, it is A who floods the kitchen and destroys the flat below.

3. C and D have been married for ten years. C suspects that D may be having an affair. D knows that C suspects that he is having an affair. He knows this because:

a. they have discussed it in a mature and rational way, laughing about how childish jealousy is.

b. every time he makes or receives a telephone call, C picks up the other phone and listens in.

c. he often sees her sitting in her car outside his office, disguised as the Queen in dark glasses and a head-scarf, on nights when he has told her that he has to work late.

4. As it turns out, D is having an affair, with a girl who was learning the basics of motor control when he was locking himself in his parents' bathroom, practising putting on a condom. He met her at an all-night service station. She couldn't get the petrol-cap off. D feels very, very guilty about this affair. He:

a. ends it quickly.

b. tries to end it at least once a week, but never quite manages.

c. writes all about it in his diary, which he just happens to leave where C can find it.

5. When C finds the diary, D:

a. says, 'It's not what you think.'

b. blames C for driving him insane with her jealousy.

c. walks out. How can he live with someone who would read his private diary? Whatever happened to trust and respect?

6. Mr E dies, leaving six adult children, a house and quite a bit of hard and soft assets. At his funeral:

a. his six children sit together, weeping.

113

b. four of his children sit together weeping, one couldn't make the funeral because of something that came up at work, and the sixth isn't speaking to the others because of an argument over fried chicken that occurred at a picnic in 1978.

c. five of his children come to blows over the coffin. The sixth is back at the house, making off with the microwave and Mr E's gold cuff-links.

7. Lorna Beetle, the Mayoress of West Westford, is in her kitchen one morning, having a nice cup of tea and listening to the radio. It is 7.47 on a Saturday. Suddenly the quiet of Mayoress Beetle's charming country town is shattered by what sounds like the stampede of two thousand wild horses, all of them wearing taps on their shoes. Mayoress Beetle, who has been awaiting an invasion since World War II, looks out of the window in some concern. But it is not two thousand wild tap-dancing horses; and it is not the resurrected Nazi army. It's the gas board. Two young men with a pneumatic drill are laying a main. Mayoress Beetle:

a. pours herself another cup of tea and turns up the radio.

b. shouts out the window that she thinks they should bloody well turn that damn thing off till a decent hour. When they don't, she puts on a pair of earmuffs, a knitted cap and a woollen scarf, and takes her tea, the radio and the morning paper into the bathroom. She gets a migraine.

c. marches into the street, shouting and swearing, her bull terriers following at her heels. When she gets to where the two young men are working, she throws a cup of tea in their faces and kicks over the drill. The dogs go for their ankles.

8. In 1986, F sold G a car. F told G that the car was worth three thousand quid, but since G was a friend she would give her a good deal on it, she would let G have it for two and a half. G is driving the car home from F's the first time it breaks down. It subsequently breaks down four times in the next week. It seems likely that it only breaks down four times because G only manages to get it started four times. F's response when G complains is to:

    a. take the car back and refund G's money.

    b. refund G's money but refuse ever to speak to G again.

    c. refuse ever to speak to G again, explaining to everyone they know that G begged her to sell her the car and is now trying to welch on the deal.

9. G is incensed. She can understand that F might not have realized what a hunk of junk she was selling her, but she can't understand why she seems to be blaming G for it. The more she thinks about it — and the more times she finds herself calling the AA at one in the morning — the more incensed she becomes. Finally, G:

    a. takes F to court.

    b. parks the car in F's front garden and leaves it there.

    c. takes an axe and a blowtorch to F's new Suzuki.

10. Years later, in 1991, F and G accidentally bump into each other in the parking lot of a major shopping centre. F is driving a new Mercedes and G a rather impressive Estate Wagon. F and G:

    a. greet each other tentatively but not with hostility. They exchange pleasantries. 'Gosh, that was a silly

115

argument we had over that car,' says F. And G agrees. 'You're right,' she says. 'I'm so glad we ran into each other. I've always felt guilty about spray-painting SLUT on the side of your Suzuki like that.'

b. pretend they don't see one another.

c. pretend they don't see one another. As soon as F sees G disappear into the shopping centre, she doubles back and lets the air out of G's tyres. At the same time, G is dropping a cement block through F's windscreen.

11. H, I, J and K are robbing a bank together. They have planned it all out in detail. H will drive the stolen getaway car. I will pass the note to the cashier. And J and K will stand guard. On the day of the robbery:

a. everything goes as planned.

b. K drops his gun on his own foot and I gives the cashier the wrong note (instead of 'This is a hold-up' it says, 'Please turn the lights out when you leave').

c. H forgets to put petrol in the car; they run out of fuel a block from the bank.

12. Miss L, a stranger in a strange land, gets into a taxi at the airport. She gives the driver the address. 'You know where this is?' she asks several times. 'You know where this is?' The driver says he knows. The driver:

a. knows. Not only does he know, but he takes Miss L there by a direct route and helps her with her bags.

b. hasn't the slightest idea where this is. Eventually, when the fare is so high that he's afraid she may not have enough money to cover it — and when the airport is looming in sight again and it occurs to him that she might recognize it — he leaves her off in front of a launderette and a billiard hall.

c. knows. He takes her there via a neighbouring principality, charges her another ten quid on top of the meter, and drives off with her suitcase.

13. Miss L is a stranger in a strange land, but not that strange. She speaks the language and has a vague idea of where she wants to go. She gets into a cab. About half-way to her destination, a small and rather disgruntled bat suddenly makes its presence known by flying at Miss L's face. Miss L assumes that the bat — who is actually trying to get out of the taxi — is trying to bite her. Miss L starts screaming pretty frantically. The driver:

a. stops the cab and comes to her assistance.

b. stops the cab, gets out, and runs for cover.

c. drives in circles for a good fifteen minutes, on the theory that Miss L is too preoccupied with the bat to notice that he's jacking up the fare.

14. M is walking home from the train one evening when she is set upon by two men who beat her up, rape her, and steal her bag. In a dazed state, M staggers into the road and flags down a passing car. The car stops. The two men in the car:

a. help M into the car, give her a jacket to cover herself, and take her to the nearest hospital.

b. decide that they don't want to get blood on the upholstery, but they offer to call the police as soon as they get to a phone.

c. put M in the car, rape her, steal her jewellery, and leave her off a few miles out of town.

15. Mr N is driving to work one day. He is tootling along, minding his own business, when Mr O suddenly appears out of nowhere, passing him across a solid line on a two-lane road and causing Mr N's heart to consider early retirement. Mr N beeps his horn and shakes his fist to let Mr O know that he is not pleased with the way he drives. He then:

    a. continues on his way to work.

    b. overtakes Mr O, and as he passes him makes a gesture extremely popular with twelve-year-old boys.

    c. follows Mr O to the next set of traffic lights and when they stop, gets out of his car and starts pounding Mr O's roof in with a tyre jack.

16. Humans land on the planet Quxqyo. There has been a highly advanced civilization on Quxqyo for thousands of years. The humans who emerge from the spaceship are carrying a flag and bearing gifts. They are anxious to find the Quxqyo word for peace. Once they've made friends with the Quxqyos and have been accepted, the humans:

    a. go back home, enriched by their experience.

    b. go back home, to return with more ships and weapons and take control, on the grounds that they are bringing the Quxqyos God and civilization. They take away anything the Quxqyos have that they consider to be of any value, and they make slaves of them. Should a Quxqyo happen to complain about this, the humans say, 'Some day you'll thank us for this.'

    c. annihilate the Quxqyos, destroy their towns and cities, obliterate almost every trace of their ancient civilization, and name a chain of petrol stations after them.

17. It is the year 2100. Despite many warnings, things on Earth have continued to deteriorate. The seas haven't been cleaned up. The forests have been turned into golf courses and tract housing. The dolphins are dead. There's a hole in the sky as big as Pluto. In desperation, Jesus Christ, the Son of God, decides to come back a second time. He arrives in a small village in the Middle East. Immediately he is:

   a. put in control of the world.

   b. asked to be on the top four talk shows and offered a merchandizing deal.

   c. shot by the CIA.

18. Jesus Christ is on Oprah Winfrey. Twenty million people watch the programme. The phones don't stop ringing. The audience is on its feet the entire time. Jesus:

   a. gives His message to the people of the world, who immediately do exactly as He instructs.

   b. receives several offers to do His chart, two movie contracts, and is mobbed and stoned by a group of radical Christians who think He is Satan.

   c. is arrested by the FBI for inciting a riot, and tragically shot by a madman who thinks He is Satan — on satellite TV — while He is being taken to his cell.

19. Mrs Alicia Patterson, eighty-two, lives by herself in a small suburban community. She has resided in this community for over thirty years. One day, not getting

any answer at the front door, the paper-boy goes round the back and sees Mrs Patterson grinding herbs at the kitchen table. He:

a. knows, naturally, that Mrs Patterson, once a world-renowned physician, is now the most influential and successful herbalist in the Western world, and takes the opportunity to ask her if she can recommend anything for his acne.

b. assumes she's senile.

c. tells everyone she's a witch.

20. Four couples, none of whom know each other well, go out to dinner together one Saturday night. Each of the couples is married. They arrive at the restaurant, order some wine, and chat pleasantly among themselves. The waitress takes their orders. They have just begun their starters when Mr Q asks Mrs Q to pass the bread. Mrs Q:

a. passes Mr Q the bread.

b. bursts into tears.

c. passes Mr Q the bread, commenting to Mr R, seated on her left, that Mr Q is going to look like a loaf of bread himself soon if he isn't careful. This causes Mr Q to make a rather sharpish remark about Mrs Q's hips and her mother. Mrs Q then proceeds to tell the entire restaurant about Mr Q's drinking problem and the time she found him in the bath-tub with her sister. Mr Q goes for Mrs Q with the salad fork.

21. Andy and Barbara are in the supermarket, shopping together. Andy puts a packet of chocolate biscuits into the trolley. Barbara, returning from an unsuccessful hunt for the tahini (it isn't with sauces, and it isn't with

120

salad dressings and mayonnaises, and it isn't with pickles, and no one employed by the store seems to know where it might be either) sees the biscuits among the brown rice, apples and muesli and goes mad. 'How can you eat that junk?' she wants to know. 'Don't you know what it does to your stomach? To your liver? To your blood sugar? Have you no regard for your teeth? Haven't you heard that chocolate biscuits cause senility, shortness of breath and contribute to pollution? It just makes my stomach turn to even think of putting one of those things in my mouth!' Andy, aware that thirteen people, four of them under the age of five, are staring at them in open wonderment, shamefacedly returns the chocolate biscuits to their shelf. Several days later, Andy and Barbara are visiting friends for tea. The hostess brings out a platter of chocolate biscuits, as well as a platter of brownies, chocolate doughnuts and chocolate fairy cakes with fudge frosting. Barbara:

a. refuses any of the cakes, explaining to her friend that they do not fit in with her ideas of sound eating.

b. says she's on a diet and eats half a biscuit.

c. scoffs the lot.

Give yourself one (1) point for every a. answer; two (2) points for every b.; and three (3) for every c.. A score of between twenty-one (21) and thirty-one (31) points shows that you have an idealized view of human nature, and are likely to find out the hard way that people make better press agents than saints. A score of between thirty-two (32) and forty-two (42) means that you have a pretty good working knowledge of the way humans *really* behave, but it is still a little flattering to them. You still want to believe they aren't so bad, and are generous in your judgement of just how far they will go. A score of forty-three (43) to fifty-two (52) means that you have had enough experience of humans to expect the worst, even though you may still be hoping for the best. Over fifty-three? It's time you went home, before it's too late.

Part Two — Survival Situations

Survival Situations

Travel, of course, is difficult enough under any conditions. No matter how many guidebooks you read or how many returned visitors you speak with, you are never as prepared as you expected to be. You may know all about the climate, how many inches of rain fall in October, what foods to avoid, and what sights to see — but what do you really know? You know nothing. You might as well go somewhere you've never heard of. There are always complications; always events you couldn't foresee. You pack your bathing-suit, and it rains for three weeks. You bring along the sun bloc and there's a revolution. You equip yourself with mosquito repellant and you're bitten by a snake. You never figure out why the waiter called you Cole Porter.

It is hoped, however, that with the help of the following true stories from aliens who have made the journey and lived to tell the tale that you will be as prepared for your visit as anyone could hope to be.

Travel

'I came, I saw, I got lost'

Akka Ka, from the planet Beezeldworp

Incredibly enough, I couldn't figure out how to get from the airport to London. The airport had seemed like the logical place to arrive, in terms of landing craft and logistics, but though I had navigated the several billion light-years from Beezeldworp to Earth, I couldn't seem to navigate the few miles from Heathrow to Kensington High Street, where friends of mine had a flat.

Every time I came to a sign, I'd stop and read it, but all the signs featured unintelligible symbols or pointed to nowhere. 'Buses' the sign might say, and then an arrow would point towards the newsagent's or a shop selling nothing but socks. I couldn't figure out if this meant that you had to go *through* the newsagent's to get to the bus, if the bus stopped in front of the newsagent's, or if there was some law about changing your socks before leaving the airport.

I started asking people where to get the Tube for London. The first few people brushed past me without hearing my question. The next few had no idea. Finally a gentleman who didn't seem to speak English pointed me towards the rest-room. I went into the sock shop. It took some time before I could get either of the assistants to break off their conversation about two friends of theirs named Hope and Michael long enough to give me any attention. 'Where?' asked the first clerk at last.

'London,' I repeated. I looked around, suddenly feeling nervous. 'This is Heathrow, isn't it?' I asked. 'I'm not in Glasgow, am I?'

The clerks exchanged a look. It was the first time I had ever seen this sort of look pass between two humans, so I had no idea of what it meant. 'You want to go to London, is that right?' asked the second clerk, not answering my question.

'Yes,' I said, hoping this signified that I wasn't at Glasgow Airport. 'I want to go to London.'

'You can get the bus right out there,' he informed me, pointing towards a juice bar.

'But I don't want the bus,' I explained. 'I want the Tube.'

'To London?' asked the first clerk.

'Yes,' I said, wondering if it was my grasp of the language that was to blame, 'to London.'

They exchanged that same glance. 'S'right over there,' they said in unison, pointing towards a wall.

I thanked them and said my good-byes.

As it turned out, 'right over there' was a stairway, leading to a ramp, leading to an escalator, leading to the Tube.

Eventually, the Tube came. There was a group of rather noisy young men already on the train when I entered. They were wearing caps and woollen scarves (although it was really quite warm and not even raining) and drinking tins of something in paper bags. They greeted me with hoots of enthusiasm and a burst of song. I smiled politely and took my seat. From what I could gather from their conversation ('Oi, this ain't the airport, is it?' they whispered to one another. 'I thought Doug was going to tell us when we got to Piccadilly Circus.'), it seemed clear that they had missed their stop. I reckoned that if they, natives of the planet, could get lost so easily I wasn't doing too badly, although it also began to occur to me that getting about might be slightly more difficult than I had thought. They woke up Doug to ask him why he didn't tell them when to get off at Piccadilly Circus. Doug threw up. I studied the map above their heads. One of the young men came over and began to tell me his life story. His father had died when he was young. His mother had married a man who didn't like him. Foreigners were taking over everything, including football. When he paused to take another drink, I asked him if he thought I should change at Hammersmith. 'What's that?' he wanted to know.

At Hammersmith, having been able to elicit no

more than a story about his girlfriend calling the police on him from my seat companion and having been rebuffed by several other passengers who seemed to think I wanted something more than information from them, I took a chance and got off the train.

Although no one on the platform seemed to know the answer to my question ('Is this where I get the District Line into town?'), a sign above my head seemed to indicate that the train I wanted would be along shortly on the same platform. I waited. While I waited, several people asked me for money, one man tried to sell me a T-shirt with the silhouette of a palm tree and the word 'Jamaica' across the front, and two elderly women in raincoats shoved me into the wall. The platform became crowded. Periodically, everyone would lean over the track and look to the left. Then they would lean over the track and look to the right. A train arrived, but it didn't stop. We all leaned over the track again and looked to the left. A woman near the stairs began to shout about not wanting to wear the pink dress to the dance. We all leaned over the track and looked to the right. And then there was a distant, crackling sound. Everyone looked up at the speakers attached to the beams over our heads. Expectantly. I was confused at first, thinking we were receiving a transmission from my ship. What were they doing, contacting me so soon? Cracklecrackleclickclackzzzzzzz. It wasn't clear enough to be my ship. And then a voice broke through the fuzz and the static. It spoke quickly, indistinctly, and in a language I had never heard before. I looked around me. No one else on the platform had ever heard this language either. There was a second's pause, and then the message — for I assumed it was a message — was

128

repeated, more quickly, less distinctly and in a different dialect. Instantly, half of the people on the platform started walking towards the stairs to the left. Everyone else stayed where they were. 'Excuse me,' I said to the couple nearest me, 'but could you tell me what the message was?'

The woman shrugged.

The man said, 'District Line's comin' in on the other side.'

The man behind him turned around. 'No it's not,' he assured me. 'Said there was a slight delay and the train would be along shortly.'

Someone tapped me on the shoulder. 'What it said was the whole line's shut down because someone jumped on the tracks and you'd be best off taking a bus.'

A rather large woman carrying something small, hairy and presumably alive under her arm joined the discussion. 'What utter rubbish!' she boomed. 'It said no such thing. What it said was that no westbound trains would be stopping at this station for the time being because of a signal failure.'

I was very confused. I explained that I was trying to get to Kensington High Street.

'Oh, you can't get there from here,' said one of my new acquaintances.

'You want to be on the other side,' said someone else.

'Take this train here,' ordered the woman with the booming voice, and she shoved me into the train that had just pulled in beside us.

Eventually, I got off at Piccadilly Circus.

The City

*'It's like being in a war someplace where the television
reception is still good and you can have pizza delivered'*

Tom, from the planet Tartuga

Being a historian specializing in intergalactic
studies, there are few places in the cosmos that I
hadn't visited. I'd been trapped in the crystal
caverns of Coper, attacked by the flickering
creatures of Shrop, caught in moon storms on
De, and walked on the dark-red air of GH2. In
short, there was little in this wild and wondrous
universe that I hadn't experienced or seen. I
considered myself a knowledgeable, sophisticated
and resourceful citizen of the cosmos, if ever
there were one.

I arrived on a New York City street corner on
an August afternoon. I was standing between a
heavyset man in a 'We Won the War for You'
T-shirt and a young couple who seemed to be
arguing. 'It's space!' the girl was shouting. 'I don't
have enough space!'

One could appreciate her point. Everywhere
else I had ever been, there had been a recognition
that in order for anything — be it animate or
inanimate — to function properly there should be
space between it and everything else. But not
here, apparently. The streets were so crowded
that it was difficult to walk. The roads were so
crowded that nothing moved. Loud music could
be heard in several different directions. Sirens
were wailing. Horns were honking. Everyone
seemed to be talking at once. I was standing in
the open in one of the largest cities on the planet,
and I felt as though I were in a space capsule with

a hairy stink-beast from Mu and seventeen
seaweed-spitting midgets from the eighteenth
galaxy. It was hot. The air was thick and
undulating. Although it was difficult to move my
arms without elbowing those next to me, I
managed to check my *Tartugan Information
Bulletin 30,456: Earth.* It said nothing about
being able to see the atmosphere. I made a note
in the margin. I took a deep breath. I checked my
bulletin again. I crossed out 'Oxygen: 20.94%'.
All at once, everyone started to walk. Not having
any choice in the matter, I walked with them. We
went into the ground.

My first thought had been that everyone was
going into the ground to get out of the heat and
the crowds. Probably, I reasoned, it was easier to
breathe beneath the surface. Cooler. More
amenable. But it wasn't. There seemed to be a lot
of $C_4H_4N_4O_3$ in the subterranean enclosure in
which I suddenly found myself. There were
certainly a lot of people. A sign said 'Subway'.
We went further into the ground. I looked up
'Subway' in *Bulletin 30,456. Bulletin 30,456*
described the subway as a 'fast and convenient
means of transportation'. But quite a few of the
people around me didn't seem to be transporting
themselves anywhere. They were sleeping on the
ground. They were asking for money. They were
going through the rubbish. They were selling
flowers from shopping trolleys. They were
playing guitars and singing. Maybe I'd read the
sign wrong. Those who looked as though they
were planning to transport themselves — that is,
those who were standing at the edge of the
platform, gazing into the tracks where rodent life
was being conducted with alacrity and
fearlessness — weren't doing it very quickly. At
last, a train pulled in. And at last something

131

reminded me of home. On Tartuga we have a small creature called the meglaphyte. Meglaphytes cluster. They are never found singly and are happiest when hundreds of them are packed together in a small space. The train pulled in and I thought to myself, *meglaphytes! They're bigger than meglaphytes,* I admitted, *and meglaphytes don't usually wear headsets or carry large appliances around with them, but they have the same instincts.* People were squashed together; people were pressed against the walls. When the doors opened the people on the platform moved forward as the people in the train moved forward. I looked up 'Physics' in the *Bulletin* and crossed out Newton's Third Law. Someone wheeled a pushchair over my feet. I decided to go back to the street.

According to *Bulletin 30,456*, the best form of transportation if you weren't sure where you were going was the taxi-cab. 'New York cab-drivers know their city the way the rest of us know the molecular structure of carbon,' said the *Bulletin*. 'They are friendly, helpful, talkative, and among the best drivers on the planet. If you don't know where you're going, take a cab.' So I did.

The cab was hotter than the street. The driver, Mr Pitu, was sitting on wooden beads and eating something that had died quite a while ago. Fuzzy dice swung from the rear-view mirror. A plastic statue stood on the dash. I gave Mr Pitu the address of the Hotel Garibaldi, which had received four stars from the *Bulletin's* assessor in 1912. Mr Pitu said, 'What's that?'

'It's the address of the Hotel Garibaldi,' I explained. 'It's in Brooklyn.'

Mr Pitu gave me a curious look. 'Where?'

'In Brooklyn.'

It dawned on me that the look Mr Pitu was

132

giving me was less curious than blank. 'Brooklyn,'
I repeated. 'It's a borough.'

'A what?' asked Mr Pitu.

I flipped to the map section of my guide. 'I
think you have to cross a bridge,' I informed him.

'Oh, *si*,' said Mr Pitu. 'A bridge.'

We went to Queens. We drove around for
some time before either of us realized that we
were in Queens. In fact, we would probably still
be driving around Queens, looking for Brooklyn,
if Mr Pitu, becoming a little nervous perhaps at
how he'd misplaced an entire section of the
metropolis, hadn't turned left into the path of a
purple limousine. The several gentlemen in the
limousine got out and started pounding Mr Pitu's
cab with assorted tools and weapons. 'Roll up
your windows!' shouted Mr Pitu.

I rolled. 'Why are they doing this?' I asked
him as the roof started moving towards us.

Mr Pitu shrugged. 'They're mad.'

It was Officers Andrews and Martell who
finally directed us towards Brooklyn. 'Christ,'
said Officer Andrews. 'It's a wonder you're not
half-way to Vermont by now.'

'Or squashed flatter than a pizza,' put in
Officer Martell.

Once we were on our way again, I told Mr
Pitu that I was sorry about the cab, which looked
as though someone had been star surfing in it.

Mr Pitu shrugged. 'At least no one will steal it
now,' he said. He then went on to tell me that he,
his wife, his six children, his three brothers, and
his aunt had all come to New York from
Guatemala, where it was hard to make a living
and easy to get shot.

'And it's better here?' I asked.

Mr Pitu crossed himself. 'It's hard to make a
living and it's easy to get shot here, too,' said Mr

Pitu, 'but the kids like pizza and at least we have a video.'

This struck me as odd. Not the part about being shot at, that seemed perfectly possible, but the part about not making money. After all, I already owed him several hundred dollars and I'd only known him a short while. 'But you have the cab,' I said. 'You must make money with the cab.'

Mr Pitu shrugged again in his philosophical way. 'It's not my cab,' he said. 'It's my brother-in-law's. He lets me use it sometimes.' He crossed himself again. 'I'm an illegal alien,' whispered Mr Pitu.

'Really,' I said. 'So am I!'

'*Amigo*!' cried Mr Pitu. He shut off the meter.

Eventually, we located Brooklyn. Brooklyn was, I assume, despite our difficulty in finding it, where it had always been, but it was not as I'd imagined. The 1912 assessor had talked of green hills and ocean breezes, quaint rural communities and elegant homes. The only green things we passed were the traffic lights. There was no breeze. The homes were elegant and the communities quaint and rural only if you came from an abandoned asteroid. There seemed to be quite a few cars without wheels parked by the side of the road. Every time we stopped at a light someone tried to sell us a blinking flower or an air freshener. 'They're illegal aliens, too,' Mr Pitu assured me.

Eventually, we found the street we wanted. It looked as though it had sustained heavy meteorite showers. We couldn't find the hotel.

'Now what?' asked Mr. Pitu.

'It must be here somewhere,' I reasoned. I suggested I get out and look.

'Not by yourself,' said Mr Pitu. 'You just got

134

here. You don't know your way around. I'll come too.'

We hadn't gone twenty feet when a new sound drowned out the distant wail of sirens.

'What's that?' I asked. 'Is someone launching a small rocket?'

'Gunfire!' screamed Mr Pitu. 'Duck!'

'Who are they shooting at?' I asked as we dived under a wheelless vehicle. 'They're not shooting at us, are they?'

'Oh, no,' said Mr Pitu. 'They're not shooting at us. They're shooting at each other.'

Bullets ricocheted off the bumpers of our hiding place.

'Well,' I sighed, 'that's a relief.'

When we got back to the cab, it was as gone as the Hotel Garibaldi.

Mr Pitu heaved another philosophical sigh. 'Why don't you come home with me and we can order a pizza and watch a video,' he suggested. 'Maybe you could help me sell snow cones in the park.'

Television

'On Earth, television is the opposite of sex. Everyone talks about having sex all the time, but no one does. No one admits to watching television all the time, but no one really seems to do anything else'

Djo Kropol, special adviser to the Starfleet Glu

In the winter of 1986, I rented a room from Alan and Hilary Budd of Streatham. I occupied the room that had belonged to their eldest son, Daniel, who had gone to university that autumn. Daniel had left behind a Wicked Willy calendar, a tennis-racket, a tank of fish, several dirty magazines under the carpet, an inflatable pitchfork, and a colour television set. I moved in on 13 December, at 5.54, having been dropped at the end of the road at 5.52. I had a cup of tea with Mrs Budd, who thought I was a foreign exchange student wanting to improve my English. Mrs Budd was watching one of her favourite afternoon programmes on her Watchman at the time. ('It's the greatest invention,' she told me. 'It means I can do the chores and not have to miss so much as a second of "Coronation Street".') At 6.30 I entered my new room. At 6.35 I turned on the television.

I didn't leave my room for five days. I watched the news. I watched documentaries. I watched talk shows and discussions. I watched films and sit coms and television dramas. I watched the soaps. I watched police dramas, variety shows, comedy showcases and commercials. How I cried with Bette Davis! How I laughed with Basil Fawlty! How I worried about JR! How concerned I was that my breath might not be fresh, that I might have dandruff, that I could never be happy without four-wheel drive!

Every morning I would turn the television on as soon as the day's broadcasting began and every morning I would turn it off when the day's broadcasting ended. In between, I sat at the window, staring out at the street and singing the catchier jingles. It looked so peaceful! More peaceful than anything on BBC1. Dogs walked along its pavements. Cats slept on its window-sills. People drove off to work, children went off to school, mothers pushed their babies to the shops, and I leaned at the window, waiting for them to start singing about chocolate or chewing-gum.

I felt confused. How did all this fit together? Out there, perhaps only metres away from tree-lined Brinkley Crescent, where the coffee tasted real, the toilets smelt like spring meadows, and mothers proved their love by keeping their families' sheets and gym socks white, were Nazi war tanks; kamikaze pilots; military actions; famine; rock stars with a social conscience; psychopathic ex-marines; cowboys; Indians; wild animals; talking cats, washing-machines and cars; singing cows, potatoes and soft drinks; dancing dustbins, waiters and packets of crisps; killers who'd had unhappy childhoods; angels who wanted to straighten out your life; sons of Satan who wanted to take over the world.

And not only that, but one couldn't depend on appearances for anything. The kindly doctor might turn out to be a werewolf. The pious priest a vampire. The police chief a drug baron. The sweet old dear down the road an enemy spy.

On the sixth day, Mrs Budd knocked on my door. 'I didn't want to bother you before, Djo,' she apologized. 'I mean, I wouldn't want you to think I was prying or anything, but you've been in there for a while love. Is everything all right?'

'Oh, yes,' I said. 'Everything's just fine.'

'Bed's not too hard?' asked Hilary. 'Room's not too warm? You figured out how to work the loo and the radiator all right, did you?'

I opened the door to show her that everything was, as they said in the black-and-white films, 'right as rain'.[27]

---

[27] 'Right as rain' was an idiom used to express the sense that everything was as good as it could or should be. Now that the rain is acid and a lot worse than it should be, this term is obsolete.

-Ed.

'But look at you!' cried Mrs Budd. 'I wouldn't want you to think I was interfering or anything, but you look so pale. Why don't you go out?'

'Out?' I repeated.

'Yes, out,' said Mrs Budd. 'You need to get some fresh air, Djo, you really do.'

According to the documentary 'How Long Is For Ever?: The Future of the Earth', it seemed highly unlikely that I would get fresh air anywhere outside an oxygen tent on this planet, but that was not my first concern. My first concern was that if I went out I might step on a minefield or be set upon by starving Samurai. Or what if I was expected to sing? I wasn't sure I knew all the words to the song about butter and low-fat spreads. 'Oh, no, really,' I mumbled, 'I like it in here.'

'Nonsense,' said Mrs Budd, 'why don't you come downstairs and have a cup of tea with me and then we can go to the shops together.'

Mrs Budd was small and neat and efficient, looking very much like the woman who poisoned lonely men in the late film the night before last.

'Oh, no,' I protested, 'I really couldn't ...'

But Mrs Budd, like Lillian, the murderess with the good intentions, was determined. 'Now, don't be shy,' she scolded me. 'You come down and have a nice cup of tea and a couple of biscuits and then we'll take a walk.'

I watched her carefully as she prepared the tea. Of course, logic told me that I had no reason to suspect Mrs Budd of wanting to poison me, after all, I'd already had one cup of tea with her, hadn't I, and though a little on the acidic side, it certainly hadn't arrested my heart. But on the other hand I had no reason to assume that she didn't want to do me in. If I'd learned one thing from my hours of telecommunications, it was that you never can tell. People are unreliable.

After Mrs Budd set our cups on the table, I changed them around while her back was turned (the way the clever hero did it in the movies) just to make sure.

Mrs Budd returned from the pantry with an unopened packet of biscuits. They were the ones with the goodness baked in. I decided to risk them.

While we had our tea, and I wondered which of the several artificial flavours I was tasting was the goodness, Hilary told me her life story. For some reason, it made me feel as though we were on a train.

'There now,' said Hilary when we'd finished our tea. 'Shall we go?'

I could only gaze at her in stupefaction. I'd become so engrossed in the details of her arguments with Mrs Murphy next door over the sexual habits of Mrs Murphy's cat, Bob, that I'd forgotten we were meant to leave the house. 'Now?' I asked.

Mrs Budd nodded. She pushed back her chair. 'Come on then,' she said briskly. 'You didn't come all this way to sit in your room, did you?'

The answer to this question, of course, was, 'No, I came to do the field work for my degree in Earth languages, but quite frankly, Mrs Budd, I'd rather stay in my room than chance being caught in a herd of stampeding bison.'

'Well ...' I said.

Mrs Budd handed me an umbrella. On television, it usually only rained in murder mysteries, thrillers, tales of domestic strife and cold-remedy commercials, but on Brinkley Crescent it rained all the time.

We proceeded to the shops.

Much to my surprise, no one shot at us as we

walked along. Mrs Budd chatted happily about whether or not Princess Di was happy, unconcerned that at any turning we might come upon a band of Apache warriors with a grudge. 'My, my,' said Mrs Budd, interrupting her concern over the Corgis' diet, 'you certainly are jittery. I think it must be that European food, don't you? It's far too spicy if you ask me. As soon as we get back to the house I'll fix you a nice cup of custard and another pot of tea.'

I followed her onto the High Street. There wasn't a tank in sight. The only animals we passed were either on leads or asleep. No one was dancing or singing or riding an elephant. But I knew, of course, that this was the time to worry most. When things seemed quiet. When you felt safe. Any second now a sniper's bullet might cut short our expedition or a piano might fall on our heads.

'It's the war, isn't it?' asked Mrs Budd as we crossed towards the supermarket. 'Your people really haven't got over it yet, have they?'

And then I saw it. Parked outside the bank was an armoured truck. Two men in what looked like gravity suits stood beside it. I knew what this meant. An ordinary shopping street. A rainy afternoon. Women with their arms filled with shopping and children coming home from school. It was a scene I had witnessed at least seven times in the past five days. The bank was about to be robbed. Robbed or blown up by terrorists. At any second, men with Russian-made machine guns and stockings over their heads would burst through the doors, trailing fear and violence in their wake.

Decades of patrolling the eighteen galaxies of the northeast quadrant had made my reflexes sharp and my ability to judge and act on a situation immediate. Without a second thought, I threw Mrs Budd to the ground, protecting her with my own body. I waited to hear the first shots; the screams of horror; the theme song from *Superman*. All at once a pain as hot as a parhelion shot through my groin. 'It must be the water,' said Mrs Budd as she pushed me off her. 'The water in Europe's never been right since the war.'

Later, as we sat at her kitchen table, eating custard and drinking tea, I explained to Mrs Budd why I had seemed to attack her and she apologized for trying to ensure that I never procreated. She laughed. 'You can't take television too seriously,' she said. 'Not that I watch that much myself,' she informed me. 'We mainly have it for the kids.'

The Dinner Party

'The dinner party is what humans do instead of having their friends to supper or writing their novels'

M_2, from the Galactic Sweeper in the Second Quadrant

During one of my visits to Earth, I worked in an advertizing agency. I had intended to get a job in television, as my purpose was to investigate deviant technology,[28] but I was unable to as there was already one female technician working in the area at the time. So I opted for a job as a

---

[28] It is only on Earth that technological progress, rather than being used to benefit the planet and all that lives on it, is used instead to support the lifestyles of the few and provide the many with things they don't need.

copywriter on the theory that television and advertizing were pretty much the same thing. My employers said I had a 'fresh eye'.

One of my colleagues (a chap I didn't know very well, who I'd always suspected didn't like me very much since whenever I said something at a meeting he would smile thinly and say, 'Well, I suppose that is one way of looking at it') invited me to dinner. 'Andina and I are having a few friends over Saturday night,' he told me, 'and we wondered if you'd be able to make it.'

I took him literally. That is, I was able to make it, as I had no previous engagements and I didn't anticipate anything physically stopping me from going. It never occurred to me that it was perfectly acceptable to make up an excuse and say no (which, I later realized, is probably what the person who was his first choice had done). 'Why thank you, Hal,' I said, 'that'd be very nice,' not aware at the time how wrong I could be.

Hal greeted me at the door, looking much the way he did when he was a day away from a deadline and had nothing new to say about dish detergent. 'Great to see you,' he said, taking his lips away from his drink just long enough to kiss the top of my ear. 'So glad you could make it. Don't you look lovely? Come on in and meet everyone.'

There were fifteen people sitting in a circle in the living room, not including the hostess, who could dimly be heard throwing things around the kitchen. Everyone was clutching a drink the way someone who has fallen off the wing of her ship while making a manual adjustment to the flaps will clutch at her safety line, and passing the nuts. As we stood on the threshold, I caught snatches of muttered conversation. 'Such nice weather we've been having ...', 'Of course, as soon as I

Where would Man be if he didn't know how to spend his time in a productive and enjoyable manner?

can, I'm quitting this job to write my novel ...',
'It's not that I'm not sympathetic to his point of
view ...', 'My mother always criticizes me,
too...', 'I wouldn't admit this to everyone, but I
do think Tolstoy's just that little bit overrated ...'

Hal stuck a glass of wine in my hand and
called out, 'Everyone this is Meg Hol ... Meg
Har ... Meg ...'

'Tue,' I offered. 'Meg Tue.'

'Meg,' he concluded. 'Meg, this is Dan, Janet,
Ellen, Lila, Ray, Terence, Burn, Natalia, Sue,
Mark, Omar, Gerry, Pauline, Richard, Steve, and
Mrs Harris.' There was a chorus of bahs from the
humans and one thin meow from Mrs Harris. I

found a place on the edge of the sofa, next to the cat, and put the same grim smile on my face that everyone else seemed to be wearing. Mrs Harris stretched, digging her claws into my thigh. I deduced from the advanced state of shredding of the side of the couch that it would be inadvisable to give her a pinch or dump her on the floor.

The woman across from me leaned over and shook my hand. 'My name's Natalia,' she smiled. 'What's your star sign?'

'Excuse me?' I said.

To tell the truth, though I had made several research trips to the planet before, I rarely socialized (it's a long story, but an uncle of mine once spent nine months in jail in Glasgow, Ohio, because he'd confused it with Glasgow, Scotland, and turned up in a kilt, an experience that had made me wary) and so had no idea what she was talking about.

'What's your star sign?' she repeated. 'I'll bet you're a Gemini.'

'Gemini?'

She took my confusion as a 'No'. 'If you're not Gemini, then you must be Cancer,' she informed me. 'I just have this feeling about you ... your aura ...'

'Aura, schmaura,' said the gentleman seated on the other side of the cat. 'All this astrology's a lot of hooey. What you want to get into is hypnotic regression.[29] Once I realized that I had

---

[29] It is yet another interesting facet of the human psyche that while the majority of people are unhappy and/or dissatisfied in their lives, they still want to be assured that they have lived before. It is equally interesting that of the millions of people who have been successfully hypnotized and returned to what they believe to be their previous incarnations, more of them discover that they were kings, great warriors, infamous beauties or Nefertiti than discover they were slaves, beggars or insurance salesmen.

been an Indian rajah I was able to completely resolve my difficulties with my father.'

'Taurus,' said Natalia, giving him a sharp look.

'The only thing you can rely on is crystals,' said the woman sitting next to the man who was once an Indian rajah in a voice so quiet it was almost a whisper. Her name was Pauline. 'They've allowed me to have several out-of-body experiences.'

He snorted. 'You don't consider recalling your past lives an out-of-body experience? Let me tell you, when I went back to the thirteenth century and realized that I was with Marco Polo on his journey to China, it put everything in my life in perspective.'

'Life is an out-of-body experience,' put in Natalia. 'That's what neither of you seem to understand.'

The smoke alarm went off.

Everyone looked towards the kitchen.

Hal appeared in the doorway. 'Soup's on, chaps,' he announced.

After I removed Mrs Harris from my chair, I was seated between Richard, the man who had been both an Indian rajah and a comrade of Marco Polo's, and Burn, a songwriter whose 1971 rock hit about love and freedom Hal had used in an award-winning car advert.

Andina, Hal's wife, emerged from the kitchen looking like she'd just waged war with the Galtrons and lost. 'I hope this is all right,' she said as she placed the soup-tureen on the table. There was something green in her hair. 'It's a recipe I cut out of *The Times*.'

There were a few bahs and a sprinkling of 'I'm sure it'll be fine's.

Marco Polo's companion leaned over and whispered in my ear. 'I hope it's not that damn cucumber soup she always makes.'

Burn started pouring the wine.

'Oh, gosh,' said Andina as she ladled out the first course. 'I do hope I didn't put too much pepper in it.'

More sheep sounds and a couple of 'Andina, don't worry, you're such a good cook's. Several hands stretched for the bread.

'Or salt,' said Andina.

'Ever eat here before?' asked Burn.

'Or mint,' Andina continued.

I shook my head.

'Better top you up then,' he winked.

'God help us,' muttered the Indian rajah. 'I smell cucumber boiled in yoghurt and flour.'

'Don't feel you have to eat it if you absolutely hate it,' ordered Andina.

Hal knocked back half a glass of red and laughed. 'Darling, don't be silly,' he said. 'Everyone's going to love it and you know it.'

I eyed the bowl.

'So you're what's her name from thingamebob,' said Richard the ruler and explorer.

I said, 'Pardon?'

'What's her name from thingamebob,' he repeated.

For one nanosecond I thought he was telling me that he knew who I really was, M_2, from the Galactic Sweeper in the Second Quadrant, but then it struck me like a light wave that he was referring to the woman who had the sense to make up a previous engagement and stay home and wash her hair. 'I'm Meg from Wiley & Wiley,' I corrected, still eyeing my soup.

'Oh,' he said, sounding disappointed. 'I thought you were the channeller.'

'The channeller?' I queried.

146

The man who had been with Marco Polo when he discovered spaghetti nodded. 'Hal said he was inviting Bettina Davis-du Menoza. She's in touch with an Aztec priest.'

'You wouldn't want to be too in touch from what I've heard of Aztec priests,' I commented.

'Have some more wine,' said the songwriter.

I poured it into my soup.

The songwriter wanted to know if I'd ever heard of him.

Temporarily forgetting that people ask you questions not to hear your answer but to hear you tell them what they want to hear, I said, 'No, I don't think I have.'

Burn started talking to Sue, who was on his other side.

Andina wanted to know if anyone wanted seconds.

Everyone wanted to save themselves for the main course.

Yet another mistake.

'Now I know we have a couple of vegetarians[30] here,' Andina apologized as Hal came out of the kitchen with a steaming platter, 'but I'm assuming none of you are the difficult kind who don't eat chicken.'

The rajah and I both reached for the wine at once.

'I do hope it isn't underdone,' said Andina as she started dishing up. 'Or overdone,' she amended.

There was the usual sound of bovine mammals

---

[30] Vegetarians, like environmentalists and pacifists, are generally looked upon with suspicion by most humans. It is assumed that if you don't like to eat the flesh of another creature, are concerned about the fate of the planet and disapprove of mass murder you must be a subversive in league with the Devil.

grazing in a meadow and several, 'Perfect,
Andina, absolutely perfect's.

Blood oozed onto my par-boiled potato and
my tablespoon of peas. I imagined the cute little
chicks in the colour film advert I'd just been
shooting, growing up just to wind up on Hal's
and Andina's wedding Wedgwood, sprinkled
with thyme. Mrs Harris bit my ankle.

'How is it?' asked Andina. 'Has anyone tasted
it yet? It's a recipe I cut out of *Cosmopolitan*.'

It was just about then that Sue mentioned Jim
Morrison. What she said was, smiling at Burn,
'When I was younger I always confused you with
Jim Morrison.'

From the other end of the table, Mark, whom
I took to be her husband, moaned, 'Oh my God,
Sue, you're not going to start with him again, are
you?'

'Who's Jim Morrison?' I asked.

There were a few hoots from around the table.
'Who's Jim Morrison? Can you believe she
doesn't know who Jim Morrison is? Where is she
from, Alpha Centuri?'

I could tell that no one was going to tell me.
Mrs Harris clawed my knee.

Burn, meanwhile, was spitting half a glass of
wine onto his plate. 'Me?' he gasped, when he'd
recovered enough to speak. 'Jim Morrison? You
confused *me* with Jim Morrison?'

Sue nodded. 'It's not the eyes,' she explained.
'Jim had those amazing, haunted eyes. But there's
something about the mouth . . .'

'He was Sagittarius,' called Natalia from across
the table.

Thinking she was referring to the planet
Sagittaria, where I'd spent quite a lot of time, I
began to say, 'I don't think he could be. I'm sure
I never . . .'

148

'He was a total moron,' Burn cut in. 'A talentless, drunken bum.' He mopped up some blood with his roll. 'That's what he was, effin' Jim Morrison. Nothing less and nothing more.'

'Excuse me,' I said, looking first to Richard, then to Natalia, then to Burn, 'but I really don't know who you're talking about.'

'He was one of the most beautiful men who ever lived,' said Sue.

'No more wine, Sue,' called Mark. 'Absolutely not one more drop.'

Terence threw his napkin on the table, glaring at Burn. 'What are you, jealous?' he demanded, reaching over and drinking down Sue's wine for her. 'Jim Morrison had more talent in his earlobe than you've ever shown in your entire career.'

Burn leaned towards him, his face quite red for a human. 'Wait a minute,' he said, with an ill-natured grin. 'Let me get this straight. *You're* telling *me* about music? You, a man who writes slogans for dandruff shampoos and lawn-mowers?' The candles flickered. His hair dangled in his wine.

'Was he a composer?' I asked.

Terence's voice was level and reasonable, which surprised me. It had been my experience that anyone drinking that much that quickly usually became a little hysterical. 'Let's not forget that it's your songs we use as background music to my slogans, mate.'

'There's one more piece of chicken left, if anyone wants it,' called Andina.

'What sort of music did he write?' I asked. Mrs Harris was half-way onto my lap. I slipped her my fowl.

Omar said, 'Get off it, Burn. You're just pissed off because that girl claimed to have seen Jim Morrison in Brighton and it turned out to be you.'

149

Lila pointed her fork at Burn. 'Jim Morrison was a god among men, and that's all there is to it.'

'He was a drug-addict and a drunk,' argued Burn. 'The best song he ever did wasn't even written by him.'

'He was gorgeous,' sighed Ellen.

Sue shook her head. 'No,' she said, in a faraway voice, 'Lila's right. He was a god.'

'Is he dead?' I inquired of no one in particular.

'What did you do to these potatoes, Andina?' asked Mark. 'I've never had anything like them before.'

'Jim was like Dionysius,' said Lila. 'He was larger than life.' She wiped away a tear. 'His death was a terrible tragedy,' she breathed.

'So he is dead,' I said.

'I steamed them,' said Andina. 'It's ever so healthy. Would anyone like some more peas?'

'Sagittarians are often troubled, and they do like to drink,' said Natalia, 'but no one can deny that they have a natural poetry and a special spirit.'

'I thought they were known for their technological brilliance,' I put in. 'We always say they have the minds of computers but the souls of dead meteors.'

Natalia scowled. 'Don't tell me you're one of these New Age astrologers,' she said, laser guns in her smile. She kicked me under the table.

Burn threw down his fork and reached for the bottle, beating Terence by a flicker. 'The only natural thing Jim Morrison ever had was a hard-on,' he raged. 'And the only spirit was Jack Daniels.'

'Darling,' said Hal, 'you've really surpassed yourself this time. The chicken is perfection in breadcrumbs.'

'I used digestives,' confessed Andina.

'You do realize that he's still alive, don't you?' asked Richard. 'Teaches symbolist poetry at the Sorbonne.'

'Give me a break,' begged Burn.

'I thought he was dead,' I protested. Mrs Harris climbed all the way onto my lap and began eating off my plate.

'Oh, sweetheart,' said Andina, 'you know you shouldn't do that.' She smiled at me. 'Just push her off if she's being a nuisance.'

I couldn't push her off. She was dug into my thighs.

'Have you seen him yourself?' Lila asked Richard.

'I saw him in a vision once,' said Natalia. 'He was in the desert, leading the Indians in a dance.'

'Were they exposing themselves?' sneered Burn.

I turned my plate around so Mrs Harris could have the potato. 'You mean he was an Indian?' I asked.

'I saw him,' whispered Pauline. 'I left my body on the night of 18 August, 1988, and I went to Tibet, and Jim was there, living by himself in the mountains and writing poetry.'

Mrs Harris started on the peas. I helped myself to more wine. I was beginning to understand why humans drank so much. 'He was a monk?'

'How did he look?' asked Lila, Ellen and Sue.

'Like a yak,' snapped Burn.

Terence threw his bread roll at Burn. 'Just because you wrote one slightly successful pop song twenty years ago, doesn't mean you can deny the fact that Morrison was a real poet,' screamed Terence.

'Do save room for pudding,' begged Andina.

Burn stood up, knocking over several glasses

and a bottle of water. 'That does it,' he shouted back. 'I'm not going to sit here with these imbeciles one second more.'

'Oh, but you don't want to miss dessert,' said Andina. 'I cut the recipe out of *Harper's*.'

Omar, Dan and Terence all got to their feet. 'Who are you calling imbeciles?' they wanted to know.

'Who the hell do you think?'

'Excuse me,' I said, 'but *who is* Jim Morrison?'

Everyone started shouting at me at once.

Later, after the police had gone, and everyone had dried off and been bandaged, Andina said, 'You know, I think next time I'll try a little sage on the chicken as well.'

Advertizing

Alice Popola, Special Emissary from Lute[123]

Lute, as you probably know, is at the centre of a roving galaxy. Sometimes we're in one quadrant, and sometimes we're in another. Sometimes there is nothing around us but emptiness, and sometimes there are so many stars that you'd think we were trapped in a jar of glitter. We may go several millennia without contact with any other life base, and then one morning we wake up and we're at a planetary convention and we're the guest speaker. Spatial chasms swallow us, astral bodies collide with us, intergalactic expedition forces can't find us. That is why the Lutian motto has always been: You can get used to anything.

It wasn't until I came to Earth that I realized this wasn't true.

I have never been able to get used to the cinema. I don't know why, I just haven't. I don't

mind that the popcorn's always cold and stale
and the lobby smells like low tide. I don't mind
those tiny little theatres, like cubicles in a
changing room. I don't mind the fact that the
people behind me always talk through the entire
film, either explaining the plot or giving it away. I
don't mind that there's always one person at the
front who laughs like a Bjorkian space pilot
who's been up for ten light-years and has had too
much helium. I don't even mind that your feet
always stick to the floor.

What I mind are the adverts.

You arrive at the Cinemaplex: seventeen
different theatres, a bar, cold popcorn,
twenty-eight kinds of chocolate[31] and the distinct
aroma of stewed pig ears. After a little haggling
with the person selling the tickets (who,
enigmatically enough, can never tell if you meant
two tickets for cinema four, four tickets for
cinema two, or if you were merely asking the
time) you gain admission. You enter the theatre.

---

[31] On Earth, there is no equivalent to the Too Much of a Good
Thing concept prevalent in most of the universe. Humans believe
that if one hamburger is good, then two will be better; one bomb
helpful in obliterating the opposition, then three thousand will be
even more effective; that if milk chocolate is popular, then plain
chocolate, white chocolate, dark chocolate, darker chocolate,
half-and-half chocolate, green chocolate, multi-coloured
chocolate, aerated chocolate, chocolate with nuts, chocolate with
raisins, chocolate with nuts and raisins, chocolate with cereal,
chocolate with chocolate chips, chocolate with caramel, chocolate
with nougat, chocolate with caramel and nougat, chocolate with a
cream centre, chocolate with a mint centre, chocolate with
coconut, chocolate with peanut butter, etc. will be even more
popular. The Lutian poet-philosopher-physicist, Myke Ike, once
jested, 'If humans spent half as much time thinking as they do
coming up with new flavours of ice-cream, the rest of the world,
not to mention the universe, would have nothing to worry about.'

You sit down. The lights dim. 'Isn't this exciting?' you whisper to your companion. 'It's always so different on the big screen.'

The big screen flickers. Your companion passes you the popcorn.

There is a long shot of blue ocean. Music begins to play, fifty-eight strings and an electric organ doing a stirring rendition of a song about personal freedom that was popular in the sixties. A stunningly beautiful young woman wearing a white swimsuit dives into the ocean. She is smiling.

You lean towards your companion. 'So what's the story about?' you whisper. 'Is this the thriller or the comedy about the housewife who is mistaken for a sex goddess who disappeared in a plane crash five years before?'

A man in a wet suit suddenly appears on the left of the screen as the ocean recedes. The man in the wet suit is standing on a cliff, gazing off into the distance with a worried expression.

'It must be the thriller,' your companion whispers back through a mouthful of cold corn. 'I can't remember now which tickets we asked for.'

'I thought it was set in Finland or Sweden or somewhere like that. It looks a little warm for Helsinki.'

One good reason to buy anything.

Your companion shakes her head. 'It probably starts in Cuba or something and then goes to Finland. You know how they like to get more than one location into these things. It makes it more exciting.'

'So is this chap the villain, or what?'

'He must be,' she decides. 'He isn't anyone famous, is he? And he's not really good-looking. I'm sure the hero's played by Bruce Willis or Mel Gibson or one of those blokes.'

'Lots of blood and great one-liners,' you say happily, reaching for the butter-flavoured snack and wondering if cinema popcorn could be considered the Redman's revenge.

Suddenly, the camera goes beneath the waves and six zebra fish and the beautiful young woman in the white swimsuit shimmer by. They're all smiling.

'This must be the girl the hero's going to fall in love with,' you comment.

Sunlight flashes off the camera lens and the music intensifies.

The man in the wet suit dives into the ocean.

'Maybe not,' says your friend. 'Maybe it's his sister or his wife and she's about to be murdered.'

You close your eyes. 'I can't watch!' you hiss. 'Tell me when I can look!'

'Wait a minute,' says your companion. 'I don't get this. They're smiling at each other.'

You open your eyes. Sure enough, the man and the beautiful young woman in the swimsuit are smiling at each other longingly, seductively.

'Oh good grief,' you murmur, poking your friend in the ribs, 'this isn't the film, it's an advert.'

She groans. 'An advert?' she hisses back. 'What for?'

'Chocolate?'

Her head shakes. 'Uh uh. The chocolate one's on dry land. Maybe it's for watches.'

Your head shakes. 'She isn't wearing a watch. If it were for watches, they'd both be wearing one.'

'Puerto Rico?' she guesses. 'The Bahamas? Ibiza? Jamaica? The Riviera? Vietnam? Cornwall?'

'It can't be for a holiday,' you point out. 'There aren't any palm trees.'

'Rum? Gin? Lager?'

'No way.' You are adamant. 'Not without palm trees or boats. Are you sure this isn't for chocolate?'

'I think it's for watches,' she says. 'Or cars.'

Another group of zebra fish dart past, as the man in the wet suit and the woman in white join hands and paddle towards the surface.

'But *she's* not wearing a watch,' you object. 'And if it were a car ad they'd be in the car, not swimming around in the coral.'

Still smiling, the couple on the screen breaks through the water.

While you're still quibbling about whether it's car music or not and trying to wrest some more popcorn from the container, the camera pans back; the scene dissolves. The film turns to black and white. A young man is getting off a bus. He is smiling.

You glance at your companion. 'Is this a different commercial?' you whisper.

The background music is also a hit of the sixties, but this one is about dancing and riding motorcycles and is played on guitars.

'It must be,' she assures you. 'Look, the girl is wearing clothes.'

The girl, who is smiling and throwing herself into the arms of the young man climbing down

156

from the bus, *is* wearing clothes.

'Jeans?' you offer.

'Alcohol,' ventures your friend.

'But they're both wearing jeans,' you say. 'It can't be alcohol if they're both wearing jeans.'

'It could be beer.' Your companion squints at the screen, thoughtfully. 'And, anyway, the couple is never together in the jeans ads. Either they've just parted, they've just met, or they're just about to meet.'

'Maybe it's for watches,' you muse. 'They *are* both wearing watches.'

'They're both wearing shoes, too,' she points out. 'Maybe it's for trainers.'

'Toothpaste?' you suggest. 'Hair gel? Deodorant?'

The couple, still smiling, disappear into a small roadside tavern. You wonder if they serve peanuts in the tavern. The camera pans back. The scene fades out.

The scene fades in. It's in colour again. You eat some more popcorn. Late sixties rock music — a song about joy and happiness — rattles the walls of the tiny theatre. A young woman in jeans, a bikini top, sun-glasses and high-heeled sandals steps out of a cherry-red sports car.

'Polaroid,' you say.

Your pal shakes her head. 'Uh uh. This one's for the car. The music's happy.'

'But there's too much drum for a car ad. I think it must be jeans. See the way the bloke at the petrol pump is eyeing her bum?'

'Maybe it is sun-glasses,' she opines, 'he's wearing them too.'

'They're in the desert.'

She shrugs. 'Definitely sun-glasses. Or beer. They do beer, sun-glasses and cars in the desert, but never jeans.'

'Oh, yes, they do,' you correct her.
'Remember the ad where the car breaks down
and this really cute bloke stops to help them?'

Your friend takes the last cold kernel from the
carton. 'I was always hoping there'd be a sequel
to that,' she says. 'You know, to see what
happened after they all got back to town.'

'You're right,' you finally decide. 'It must be
for the car. Now he's looking at the car the same
way he was looking at her bum.'

'Wait a minute,' your seat-mate cautions.
'There's a dog. That changes everything.'

'Not necessarily,' you logic. 'If it was for dog
food they would have brought the dog on earlier.'

'Not always,' she argues. 'Not if they're
targeting a younger dog owner.'

It isn't until the title rolls across the screen that
you realize you've been watching the feature film
for the last ten minutes. 'So what was it?' you ask
your friend. 'The thriller or the comedy?'

She throws the empty popcorn carton on the
floor. 'I was hoping you'd know,' she sighs.

Work

'Work is what you do to pay the mortgage, so that when
you die your children will be able to sell the house and go
to Hawaii for a week and a half'

BuBu Patu, Overseer of the Development of the Asteroid X*X^6

In one of the most popular films on this planet of
all time, seven little men with pickaxes over their
shoulders march off to work every morning
whistling and singing. We used to detour Earth
transmission of this film a lot when we were

constructing X^*X^6, watching it after our own
labours were done. 'What a place of marvels
Earth must be,' we used to comment to one
another. 'People have such a good time at work.
Not only does it give them a sense of personal
value and fulfilment,[32] it makes them happy.' I
couldn't wait to go there and get a job.

I got work in a plant that manufactured
running shoes. After the shoes came off the
assembly line, my job was to put the laces
through the first two holes.

The first thing that I noticed was that everyone
was much taller than I'd expected them to be.

The second was that no one sang or whistled
as we walked through the gates every morning.

'My God,' groaned my work-mate Jerome. He
put his head in his hands. Sounds of the pulsating

[32] Dr Sigmund Freud's contribution to the twentieth century as
the man who made a lucrative profession out of doing what
wives, mothers, mistresses, whores and bartenders had been
doing for nothing for centuries (listening to other people's
problems and giving them bad advice about them) cannot be
overstressed. Besides inventing psychoanalysis and penis envy, he
emphasized the importance of work to the well-being of the
psyche. Man, said Freud, needs work to be happy. Naturally, no
one on Earth any longer remembers exactly what Freud had in
mind when he spoke of 'arbeit', but it is taken nowadays to mean
employment. Elsewhere in the cosmos, of course, there is a
distinction made between work one does because it has to be
done (e.g., spending three months building an environment dome
on X^*X^6, only to discover that one has put it in the wrong place
and has to start all over again on the other side of the crater) and
work one does because it gives one inner peace, satisfaction and
the indefinable joy usually associated with watching the moon
storms over Sillup Sillup (e.g., spending seven years planting and
tending a garden on X^*X^6 and sitting out there for hours holding
protective sheeting over the bluebells during the meteor season).
On Earth, however, one is meant to be fulfilled by selling car
phones all day, and then go home and watch TV.

Work gives life meaning.

ooze of the Inner Megalwi swamp issued from his
mouth. I looked down to make sure there were
no smallish green and purple reptiles darting
around my feet.

It was the end of my first week at the factory,
and Jerome and I had stopped off at the pub for
a beer on our way home. 'What's the matter?' I
asked as I set the second round on the table. 'Is
the carpet giving you a headache?'

Jerome raised his eyes to mine, 'No,' he
sighed, 'it's not that. It's because it's Friday.' He
groaned once more. 'Fridays always depress me.'

This puzzled me, as, much to my surprise,
everyone else at the plant had seemed
inexplicably cheered and cheerful over the fact
that it was Friday. 'Because you're going to be
away from work for two whole days?' I asked.

Jerome gazed at me over the top of his drink.

'You what?' he asked.

'Because you won't be back at work for two days?' I repeated.

'Well, sort of,' said Jerome, eyeing me as an atom might regard a wayward electron. 'Though I think I might change the words "you won't" to "you will".'

I sniffed thoughtfully at my packet of ketchup-flavoured crisps. 'I don't understand,' I confessed.

'Get us another beer and I'll explain,' said Jerome.

Jerome said that he used to hate Mondays. He'd wake up on Monday morning and he'd think, *Lord help me, I've got to go back to work.* But he'd loved Fridays. He'd wake up on Friday morning and he'd think, *Praise the Lord! Two whole days to do as I please*! Over the years of inspecting the soles of women's running shoes, however, two whole days were whittled down to 'two days' and then 'just two days', until finally he hated Fridays because they came right before Mondays.

'I guess that explains why no one sings or whistles while they work,' I said when he had finished. 'I'd been wondering about that.'

'Sing?' squawked Jerome. 'What are you talking about, "sing"? Are you off your rocker? What have we got to sing about?'

I picked up my pint, trying to remember if this was the third or the fourth. 'Work?' I suggested.

Jerome spat a mouthful of Special Brew across the table. 'Sing about work?' he choked. 'You mean like a dirge?'

'No,' I explained. 'Like in *Snow White and the Seven Dwarfs*.'

Jerome stared back at me with the same expression he wore as he inspected men's soles. It reminded me of nothing so much as a gap between stars.

'You know,' I insisted, 'like in Freud? Work is necessary for the happiness of man?'

Jerome started laughing again. 'I don't know about Snow White,' he chortled, 'but Freud was full of crap if you ask me. Work may give your life meaning if you're sitting in a room listening to some bloke tell you the dreams he has about his mother — though to be frank with you, mate, I'd be hard put to tell you just what that meaning might be — but it don't mean anything but a couple of quid at the end of the week if all you do for seven hours a day is check the thickness of a slab of blue rubber.'

'It doesn't make you feel useful and productive?'

'Women's runners?' asked Jerome. 'BuBu, they make 150 new styles every year. That means they expect women who already own perfectly good shoes to go out and buy at least one new pair every few months just because this season's model has studs on them or orange trim. How useful and productive does that make you feel?'

'It doesn't give you a sense of purpose and direction?'

Jerome shrugged. 'I suppose it directs me off the streets,' he admitted.

'Well, how would you define work, then?'

That look of the dark emptiness between two distant points of light came into his eyes. 'It's what I do when I'm not sleeping, eating, or watching the telly.'

'What about the unquenchable thirst of the human spirit for joy and beauty, self-expression and identification with the universal life force and essence of creation?'

He winked. 'Around here they call it beer.'

Shopping

'Shop till you drop'

Lydia Mercedes, student from Venus II

I was staying with the Whistledowns of Cherry
Lane, Chiswick. Mrs Whistledown was very
involved with charity work and it was her idea to
take me in when the woman I had been boarding
with, an old friend of my Uncle Ben, was arrested
for dumping a ton of sludge in the car park of a
company that trades in toxic wastes. The
Whistledowns had a daughter near my age (I was
eighteen on Earth), a sixteen-year-old named
Penelope Grace.

Penelope was usually busy with school,[33] her
boyfriend, parties, talking on the telephone,
listening to music while she pulled the hair out of
her legs with strips of waxed paper, or looking in
the mirror, but on my third Saturday at the
Whistledowns', I woke up to find her lying across
the foot of my bed.

'Penny?' I called.

There was no movement, no sound from the
prone figure with her face in my bedspread.

'Penny?' I leaned forward and gently shook
her by the shoulder. 'Penny? What are you

---

[33] Education is another of those things on Earth that is talked
about significantly more than it is done. Adult humans seem to
feel that if you can get a child to dissect a frog, memorize a
certain amount of misinformation regarding world history and
read one play by William Shakespeare (who many people believe
was someone else) that the child neither likes nor understands
and will proceed to misquote for the rest of her life, she is
educated. Non-adult humans, on the other hand, largely regard
school as the thing that interferes with their social lives.

doing? Is something wrong?'

'Umbiffelded,' whispered Penny.

I said, 'Excuse me?'

She raised her head. Her eyes were dull and dark. The corners of her mouth hung down in the suffering and defeat of a being who has lived fifty years stranded on a barren planetoid where the only transmissions s/he can receive are repeats of *My Favorite Martian* from Earth.

'I'm depressed,' said Penny in a hoarse, choked voice.

How could I fail to be concerned? 'What is it?' I asked. 'Do you want to talk about it? Do you want me to speak with your parents? Is there something I can do?'

Penny rolled over on her back. 'I want to go shopping,' she said.

'Shopping?'

'Yes,' she said. 'It's the only thing that will cheer me up.'

It may surprise you to learn that this did not surprise me. I was getting used to the way things worked. For instance, you might think that the answer to the question, 'What can I get for the billionaire who has everything?' would be 'Several dozen homeless children' or even 'Ethiopia'. But it's not. It's, 'A gold toothpick or computer football.' Thus, it made a weird sort of sense that Penelope, a girl with enough clothes in her wardrobe to set up her own charity shop, would consider the purchase of another T-shirt with the silhouette of a palm tree and the legend 'Calvin Klein' on it an antidote to sadness and despair.

It may further surprise you to learn that I had never been shopping before. Not that I hadn't been to the supermarket or the corner shop, I had been to both on several occasions. But I had

Shopping cures depression, headaches, boredom and that nagging sense of futility.

never been to a clothes shop, or a department store, or a shopping centre. My uncle's friend, Bryn, never bought anything she didn't need — a practice inconsistent with the concept of serious shopping — and when she did buy something she usually bought it in the thrift shop or the church jumble-sale.

Mrs Whistledown decided to come with us. Not that she was going to buy anything. 'I'm not buying anything,' she told us. 'I'm just going to look.'

Mrs Whistledown drove, and Penny directed. Mrs Whistledown couldn't drive *and* find her way at the same time, because she had to concentrate intensely. She had to concentrate so intensely because she had been taught how to operate a motor vehicle by Mr Whistledown. Being taught by her husband had made her nervous and insecure. Loud noises made her jump. Honking horns made her twitch. The sound of a male voice shouting brought her instantly to tears.

We passed the shopping centre four times, without ever finding a road that actually lead to it. 'I'm sure it's around here somewhere,' Mrs Whistledown kept muttering to herself. 'Penelope, isn't the road around here somewhere?'

Penelope, who'd been leaning out of the window, checking her eye make-up in the side-view mirror, turned to her parent. 'Don't we usually go through a roundabout?' she asked. 'Or is that when we go to the furniture shop?'

When at last we found the roundabout, Mrs Whistledown went six times around that, trying to figure out which exit would lead us to the shopping centre described by her navigator as 'out of this world, Lyd, you've never seen anything like it'.

'Are you sure it isn't the one that says North?' asked Mrs Whistledown.

Penelope started brushing her hair. 'How should I know?' she demanded. 'I'm not the driver.'

'But you are the navigator,' snapped her mother.

The horn of an impatient driver, tired, no doubt, of the way Mrs Whistledown would head towards an exit then suddenly veer back, sounded behind us. 'Oh shut up, you imbecile!' shouted Mrs Whistledown. 'What do you want me to do? Fly?'

Penelope leaned out of the car and gave him the finger.

Mrs Whistledown finally chose North, because if she didn't we were going to be run off the road.

'Look!' I cried. 'There's a sign for the shopping centre!'

Frowning with concentration, Mrs Whistledown sailed past the turn-off for the centre. The next thing any of us knew, we were on the motorway and headed towards Luton.

'Now look what you've done!' Mrs Whistledown screamed at her only child. 'Why didn't you tell me to turn left?'

'Me?' Penelope shouted back. 'Me? Lydia told you she saw the sign. Why are you blaming *me*?'

We were picking up speed. 'You were supposed to tell me when to turn!' wailed Mrs Whistledown.

'Um, excuse me,' I said, 'but isn't there a speed-limit[34] on this road?'

We overtook a lorry with flashing lights and a laughing demon and the legend 'Hell on Wheels' painted on the door. I clutched my seat-belt.

Penelope folded her arms across her chest and turned her face to her open window. 'You always

---

[34] Like the Ten Commandments, speed-limits seem to exist solely to give humans something to break. Should you be naïve enough to stay at or below the posted speed, every other vehicle on the road, except the milk-float, will zoom past you. If they can't zoom past you because you are in a single lane and there is oncoming traffic (though this, it should be noted, isn't always the deterrent you might expect it to be), they will honk their horns, flash their lights, and call you every name under several suns. It has even happened that, stopped at a traffic signal, the driver forced to go thirty when he wanted to go thirty-five (and thus reach the red light first) will get out of his vehicle, approach the driver who was obeying the speed-limit, and start beating his car with a cricket bat, tyre jack or other suitable implement. (There was even a time in America, in fact, when drivers forced to wait in long petrol queues took to shooting one another, but that was considered aberrational behaviour so we need not go into it here.)

blame me for everything! Everything is always my fault!'

'I say,' I said as the landscape blurred, 'perhaps they have a shopping centre in Luton. That would be lucky, wouldn't it?'

At almost the exact same instant, Mrs Whistledown and her daughter Penelope Grace burst into tears.

More by luck than skill or intent, we eventually landed in Car Park F.

'I don't know why you couldn't park closer,' Penny complained.

Mrs Whistledown was daubing foundation, lipstick, blusher and eye-shadow on her face, in an attempt, apparently, to make herself look normal.[35] 'I couldn't *get* any closer,' she growled. 'None of the roads lead anywhere near the bloody place.'

Myself, I was so happy that we'd stopped that I wouldn't have minded if we'd parked in Luton. 'This is just great,' I assured her. 'Look! You can actually see the building from here.' And indeed, there in the distance, shimmering in the haze attendant upon being located in the middle of a major motorway, was what looked like a Slipvokian fuelling station.

Penelope kicked the side of the car. 'I don't believe this!' she wailed. 'We have to walk miles and it's hot and everything.' She kicked the car again.

---

[35] It is one of Earth's ironies that 'normal' consists of making yourself as unlike yourself as you possibly can without minor surgery. It is another that human beauty should be so closely associated with death for so many other species. One can only assume that if Bambi's mother had been captured by make-up manufacturers and killed in the course of testing out lip-gloss, every eye in the theatre would be as dry as the Sahara.

'Don't do that!' Mrs Whistledown ordered. 'Do you know how much this car cost?' She slapped her only offspring on the head.

'Oh come on now,' I said, trying to lighten things up a little. Previously — having lived with a single and unusually rational woman and receiving my ideas of domestic life from television — I had been under the illusion that the human family was a happy, well-balanced and safe harbour in an otherwise rough world. Three weeks with the Whistledowns, however, had pretty much set me straight about that. 'It's not really miles and as it's rather late in the afternoon it isn't really hot either.'

No one was listening to me.

'I'll do what I want!' yelled Penelope, giving the Range Rover another swift kick. 'And you can't stop me!'

'Oh, no?' shrieked her mother as she whacked her over the head with her handbag. 'We'll just see about that.'

They both started crying again.

As soon as we stepped out of the smog and heat of the car park and into the air-conditioned splendour of the centre, Penny and her mother began to perk up.

'Thank God we finally made it!' they exclaimed as one.

'Let's go and look at shoes,' said Penny, heading off in one direction.

'Let's get a cup of tea first,' said Mrs Whistledown, heading off in another.

I gazed around me in wonder. I'd been expecting the high street, with a roof and benches, and minus the pigeons. But it was nothing like the high street. It was a dozen high streets, all stuck one on top of the other and packed into a theme park. There were fountains.

There was music. There were people dressed as gorillas, rabbits, and pastel-coloured bears handing out fliers and samples of chocolate and biscuits. Balloons and budgerigars drifted over our heads. Everywhere I looked there were people. People walking. People sitting. People eating. People staggering under a small mountain of carrier-bags. People screaming or crying or slapping their children around.

'Isn't this fun?' laughed Penny.

I felt weak. Weak and headachy. Mrs Whistledown's idea of a nice cup of tea was becoming attractive.

'Come on, Lydia!' Penny commanded, her cheeks flushed and her eyes bright with excitement. 'Let's shop!'

I lost count after the fifth shoe shop and the sixth clothes shop. I couldn't tell them apart. The shoes were all the same. The clothes were all the same. The sales assistants were all equally rude and unhelpful. It reminded me of the false planet of Ururu, where the atmosphere repeats

The shopping centre: a controlled environment combined with multi-level spending.

everything you see or experience over and over until it's impossible to separate the image from the real.

And, too, Penelope Whistledown was hard to please. 'I need to find something that's *me*,' she'd say. 'Something that tells the world who I am.' Sixteen pairs of shoes would be tried on, and sixteen pairs rejected because they weren't *her*. The seventeenth would be rejected because nobody was wearing that style anymore. 'What are you trying to do?' Penny would shriek. 'Make me look like a misfit?'

What seemed like eons later, tired, bedraggled, and listing under the weight of several skirts made in China, several tops made in India, and a pair of musical trainers made in Korea, Penny and I set off to find Mrs Whistledown. She was sitting at a table in one of the several cafes (all of which, needless to say, looked exactly alike and served the same food), sipping a cup of tea. She was surrounded by carrier-bags. She, like Penny, looked very happy.

'Wait till you see what I got,' she cried excitedly.

'But Mrs Whistledown,' I said, 'I thought you weren't going to buy anything. I thought you were just going to look.'

Mrs Whistledown patted my hand. 'Oh, I didn't *buy* anything,' she said with a delighted smile. 'It was all on sale!'

As we were leaving the centre, I asked Penny what all the teenagers just sitting on benches together were doing.

'Nothing,' said Penny.

'They aren't waiting for someone?'

She shook her head. 'Uh uh. They're doing nothing.'

'They aren't trying to get into a certain shop?'

Penny made a face. 'Jesus, Lydia,' she said. 'What's with you? They're not waiting for anything. They're just sitting there.'

'Why?' I asked.

She made another face. 'Because it's something to do.'

The Wedding

It is not inevitable, of course (as they like to say on Earth, nothing is inevitable but diets and television commercials), but chances are that if you stay on this planet long enough you will, at some point, be invited to a wedding.

What is a wedding?

There are, in fact, several answers to this question:

1. The ritual in which a woman and a man formally join their lives and commit themselves one to the other for as long as they both live.
2. The party celebrating this ritual (an event which has sometimes been known to last longer than the marriage itself).
3. The most important day in a woman's life.[36]

'After all,' people are fond of saying, 'you only get married once.' This, of course, is statistically untrue. Most people nowadays get married at least two or three times. You might assume that by the second or third wedding a person might be opting for the quiet ceremony and vows that speak of 'for as long as we can stand each other' rather than 'to death do us part',

[36] Interestingly enough, no one has ever suggested that it might also be the most important day in the life of a man. Most human males seem to consider this day to be the one on which they first used their penis with something other than their hand, saw Betty Luton do the harmonica breakdance, made/won/stole a lot of money, or drank a bottle of whisky and recited *The Charge of the Light Brigade* till there wasn't a dry eye on the bus.

but you'd be wrong. No matter how many times a person marries, s/he always carries on as though this is the first and last.

4. Expensive.
Because this is the most important day in a woman's life, and because a person only marries once, the people who cater to weddings — like the people who service the government — always charge at least three times what anyone else would consider paying (e.g., if the army needs to buy 3,000 gross of copper-headed screws, the army will happily pay six pence a screw, where anyone else would pay two pence). Likewise, the dry chicken and reheated rice dinner that you might consider paying three pounds for in Linda's Cafe will cost Linda's father twenty-five quid a head at her wedding.

5. The day the bride's sister finds her husband in the toilet with one of the bridesmaids and sues for divorce.

What can you expect?

Big wedding or small wedding; wedding with a marquee and a string orchestra or wedding in the church basement with Mrs Marshall on the honky-tonk piano, all weddings follow a similar pattern of play.

1. Someone will be late.

This someone is quite often the groom.

The groom may be late because his friends took him out the night before to drink a litre of whisky, watch women dance to 'Brown Sugar' in their underwear, and later throw up in the car park of The Green Man. He may be late because he couldn't get his tie done up. Or perhaps the best man, who was also at the stag party, couldn't remember where he put the ring, the car, or the groom. And, too, it could just be a case of nerves. Although in most Western civilizations the groom is well-acquainted with the bride beforehand — although, in fact, he has probably professed his love for her on more than one occasion and is very fond of her spaghetti bolognese and her back-rubs — it is not uncommon for a man to wake up on the morning of his wedding and be overcome with terror, on whose heels panic is treading. No one knows why this is so. Especially not as it is usually the man who asks the woman to marry him. Suffice to say that just as a perfectly reasonable man may punch a hole in the wall or throw all of his wife's possessions on the lawn because he discovers that she had lunch with some chap she knew at school, a man who has begged a woman to marry him and be his wife may awake on the morning of the Big Day with no thought in his mind but to head for the hills. Most grooms do not, of course, head for the hills. Most of them head for the duvet or the local pub, where, when he finally regains consciousness himself, the best man will find him, eventually managing to get him to the church.

This someone is quite often the bride.

The bride — who has usually stayed in the night before her wedding, worrying about whether or not the caterer is going to turn up or if the flowers will be the right shade of blue — rarely has to grapple with a hangover or the condolences of her friends over the fact that she will now have to ask for permission to go to a football game. What she has to grapple with is sobriety. Sometime in the wee hours of the morning, the bride wakes up from a dream in which she was chained wrist and ankle to a man who cracked his knuckles when he was bored and laughed at his own jokes. It is then that she realizes that she is about to select as the father of her children a man who does both those things. Not only that, but his favourite

174

singer is Frank Sinatra. When he's happy he plays
Frank Sinatra. When he's depressed he plays Frank
Sinatra. He hums Frank Sinatra songs when he's
bored. She snaps on the bedside lamp. 'Oh my God,'
she says to the night. 'If we're one of the thirty per
cent of couples who stay married, I'm looking forward
to a good fifty years of 'I Left My Heart in San
Francisco'. On the other hand, the wedding is
scheduled to take place in only eight hours. The hall
has been rented. The dress has been bought. The
guests have been invited. She's lost ten pounds so she
can fit into her dress. Her hair has been cut, dyed and
starched. There are 500 miniature quiches and ten
pounds of liver pâté in the shape of wedding bells in
the fridge and 500 matchbooks that say Edward and
Amber 1 June 1992 in the boot of the car. She can't
call it off now. When dawn breaks, she rises. She
begins to get ready for the happiest day of her life.
Five minutes before the car arrives to take her to the
church, she locks herself in her room. She will come
out when she realizes that if she doesn't go through
with this wedding her father will probably make her
pay for the pâté herself.

2. Someone will get very drunk.

Actually it is not unheard of that out of a wedding of
some 200 guests, 150 will get very drunk. Half of
these people will want to toast the bride and groom
for several hours, and the other half will want to tell
amusing stories about them or wonder if they had to
wed. Because so many of the guests will be higher
than a satellite, there is always a chance that there will
be someone passed out in the toilet or over the bonnet
of your car. There is also something about the combination of champagne and the hormones produced
by attending a marriage ceremony that makes humans
sexually active in much the way that global war does.

Never agree to accompany someone to the bushes or the broom cupboard.

It is also not unheard of for the bride or groom to get very drunk, not that anyone could blame them. Never assume, however, that just because a person still has rice in her or his hair that s/he won't ask you into the broom cupboard.

3. Someone will cry.

Actually, at any given wedding it is guaranteed that several people will cry.

One of these is certain to be the mother of the bride. Non-humans often assume that the mother of the bride cries at her daughter's wedding because she is so sad to lose her. The truth, however, is that the bride's mother has been waiting since the bride's eighteenth birthday to get her out of the house. No more whining or demanding. No more wet towels left on the floor of the bathroom. No more notes left on the kitchen table: Mum, Don't forget to pick up my things from the dry cleaners during your lunch-hour. No more tantrums when there isn't any diet cola in the fridge or someone else wants to use the phone. The bride's mother is so happy to finally be rid of her that, naturally, she is overcome with guilt. If anyone — especially the bride — knew for how long and with what anticipatory joy she has been waiting for this moment — the moment when her daughter became someone else's telephone bill — they would think she was a bad mother. She cries because she thinks they might be right.

The reasons the mother of the groom sobs softly through the ceremony are similar to those of the bride's mother, but not identical. Seeing the groom standing at the altar, grinning like a gargoyle, has reminded his mother of how much like his father he is. It is then that she remembers the statistics on first marriages. Only thirty per cent will survive. There isn't a doubt in her mind that her son's will not be part of that thirty per cent, not with his temper and his obsession with ziploc bags. The mother of the bride knows that if the marriage doesn't work out, her daughter will get a cat and take a flat on her own or move in with a friend. The mother of the groom knows that he'll come back home. There she'll be, with her feet up on the sofa and cracker crumbs down her front, and all of a sudden there'll be a knock at the door. When she opens it her son will be there with his luggage and the stereo. 'Just for a few days, Mum,' he'll say, and that'll be it for the next five years. He'll come back home, he'll put everything in the house in a ziploc bag, and he'll lie on the sofa every evening watching Monty Python tapes.

The bride's friends will weep buckets. Again, the uninitiated may assume this is because they are so

The most popular form of human celebration.

happy for the bride. It is far more likely, however, that it is because they know more about the groom than she does.

There is always one female friend of the groom who spends quite a bit of time in the ladies', sniffling, wiping the tears away, and repairing her make-up. This is the woman who feels she should have married the groom instead of the woman who did. It is wholly possible that, given enough champagne, she may announce this fact to the entire wedding. In which case quite a few more people will be crying before the day is done.

4. Someone will wonder whether or not the bride is pregnant.

This person could be anyone. A friend of the bride, or even a close female relative. Several friends of the groom. A next-door neighbour of the bride's family, invited only because she offered to bake the cake. It is interesting, of course, that though humans believe fervently in marriage and focus their lives on it, they find it difficult to accept that a couple might marry simply because they wanted to.

5. Someone will have a temper tantrum.

This person is usually no one connected to the wedding couple by either blood or marriage.

This person is usually the photographer. There is something about getting five hundred drunken people in varying states of good humour and aggression to stand still, look at the camera, and smile that can snap the patience of even the seasoned professional. Somewhere between the first dance and the last toast, there will come the moment when Aunt Jane asks him to take just one more picture of the bride dancing with Uncle Jeff — no from the left side — and the next thing you know film canisters are being hurled left and right and the bride is in tears because there isn't going to be a photographic memory of her and her new husband cutting the cake.

This person can also be the caterer, a member of the band, or one of the waiting-staff. None of these people really want to be at this wedding, all of these people have been at at least 560 weddings exactly like this one, have said the same things, sung the same songs, served the same food, and heard the same jokes. It is no wonder that when asked to play 'Whiter Shade of Pale' for the thirteenth time something inside the guitarist snaps.

What can you do?

1. Stay sober. Since this is something no one else will be doing — except the waiters, the caterers, the band and, maybe, the photographer — it gives you an advantage. Not only will you be unlikely to wander out of the Eventide Room, where the Butler-Meckley reception is being held, and into the Orange Blossom Room, scene of the Wyatt von Schultz party, and not be able to tell them apart (spending two hours speaking to a woman you believe to be Beverly Butler's Aunt Celia about her gallstones only to discover that she is actually the Aunt Celia of someone you've never heard of), but it will also ensure that should the best man ask you to accompany him to the broom cupboard, you will probably have the presence of mind to say no.

2. Stay sober. Somewhere around the time that the bride and groom join the band on stage to sing a rousing chorus of 'Stop in the Name of Love' you are likely to feel a great need to drink several glasses of champagne in quick succession. Resist it. You think it will make it possible for you to cope better with what you see going on around you — the bride and groom

suddenly becoming karaoke singers and the mother of the bride doing the twist with the father of the groom — and what you know is about to come — a speech by the mother of the groom about how happy she is that her son didn't marry his last girlfriend — but it won't. All it will make you do is think you can dance in high heels, which you can't.

3. Stay sober. There will come the time, round about when the best man is telling a story about going skinny-dipping with the groom (and how amusing it was when someone stole their clothes and the two of them had to walk back to town covering themselves with branches), that you will think three stiff brandies seem like a good idea. But they aren't. One minute you'll be feeling that reassuring warmth hit your stomach, and the next you'll be on the floor with the maid-of-honour, helping her collect her false nails.

4. Stay sober. If you aren't sober, you won't be able to stay awake when the people on either side of you at dinner take it in turns to tell you their life stories.

Addendum

Places to Go and Things to Do

In 1954, having lost contact with their mother ship for three tellurian years, five officers from Lixton-3 were finally relocated in a motel room in Tennessee. Except for occasional trips to the diner across the road for ham and black-eyed peas and bottles of pop, the Lixtonians had been in that room for two and a half years. They had stayed in room 3 of the Dixie Pride Motel for so long because of the six months they'd spent in Philadelphia before that. It had been both so boring and so terrifying that they'd decided they'd rather watch life on Earth on television than actually participate in it.

But for those of you who want to experience the planet and its inhabitants first hand, we have compiled a short guide to some of the more interesting places and activities.

SYMBOLS AND ABBREVIATIONS

Things to Do

†	can be worthwhile
††	not to be missed
†††	could only happen here
††††	not for the faint-hearted
†††††	proceed with caution
††††††	rarely worth the danger, the trouble, or the admission price, watch it on TV

---

†††††††	life extending [in the sense that it seems to make time stand still]
††††††††	no one will believe you anyway
†††††††††	this falls into the category of the unspeakable in pursuit of the uneatable

Places to Go

*	not to be missed
**	interesting
***	remarkable
****	unbelievable, but worth the danger
*****	not worth the danger, read about it
******	not worth the danger, the trouble, or the admission price, watch it on TV
*******	only interesting if you enjoy black holes
********	no one will believe you anyway

Practical Information

1 bring a book
2 bring a tent
3 customs vary
4 could end in tears
5 always takes longer than you think
6 you can never get there from where you are
7 remember those three-headed Alminitrons in the Lactal galaxy?
8 wear warm clothes
9 bring an umbrella
10 don't forget your boots
11 it doesn't matter what you say, because no one's really listening
12 the historical significance of this, though spoken of often, has been totally forgotten
13 myth
14 doesn't wash out

15 just say, 'No, thank you,' and get into a different
   time warp as quickly as you can
16 when Einstein said, 'I cannot believe that God plays
   dice,' he'd forgotten about this

Things to Do

Read a newspaper — †††/†††††/4,12,13
(Most newspapers on Earth contain no news. What they
do contain are a lot of stories about vicars, pregnant
schoolgirls, unhappy film stars, and the operations of
famous people. Reading the paper gives you something to
do while you're riding on a bus, and later you can use it to
line the budgie's cage.)

Go fishing — †††††††/1,2,4,8,9
(Fishing is a popular activity for male bonding because
you can't talk while doing it, but you can drink and lie
about it afterwards.)

Attend a football game — ††††/††††††/†††††††††/
3,4,9
(The major difference between American football and
soccer is that in the former the physical violence is
contained on the field, and in the latter it occurs princi-
pally among the spectators.)

Take up fox-hunting —- †††/††††/†††††††††/5,6,12
(Fox-hunting, like mud wrestling, is less a sport than a
definition of class.)

Go on a picnic — ††††/1,2,3,4,5,9,14
(As these things go, it beats both fox-hunting and mud
wrestling as a way of passing time.)

Climb a mountain — ††††/†††††/†††††††/4,5,6,8,9
(Your first question regarding this activity is likely to be:

183

'Why would I want to climb a mountain? There's nothing to see when you get up there, and then you have to climb down again.' The answer most humans would give you is: 'Because it's there.' As this is also the answer you'll receive if you ask George why he ate the joint of beef and the half a chocolate cake in the fridge, you can make of it what you will.)

Jump from a plane without a parachute — ††††/†††††/
††††††/†††††††/††††††††††/1,4,7,9,14,16
(Sky-diving is what humans do when they're not into alcohol or drugs.)

Ride down a raging river in a rubber dinghy — ††††/
†††††/††††††/†††††††/††††††††††/
1,4,5,6,8,9,10,11,14
(White-water rafting is the other thing they do.)

Learn to drive — ††/†††/†††††/3,4,9,16
(You will never truly understand human behaviour until you have had six drivers shouting, cursing and beeping their horns at you because you were too slow in starting when the light changed.)

Go to a party — ††/†††††/†††††††/††††††††††/1,2,4,
11,14
(One should be enough.)

Go to a meeting — ††/†††/††††/†††††††/1,4,5,11,12,
15
(One of these should be enough, too. Attending a meeting — any meeting — will answer that millennium-old question: Why does everything on Earth either never get done or go wrong?)

Visit an amusement park — †††/††††/††††††/†††††††
††/4,7,11,14
(Many humans feel that they haven't lived until they've

defied death on the double-twister hurricane or sat on the lap of Mickey Mouse, but you may not share these sentiments.)

Go camping — ††††††/†††††††/††††††††/1,2,3,4,5,6,7,8,9,10,13,14,15
(Camping is one of Man's attempts to get in touch with his primitive self, but from the vantage point of a five-hundred-pound tent and air mattress. Whether or not you'll enjoy it probably depends on how eager you are to touch the primitive self of Man.)

Go to a sale — ††/†††/††††/††††††††/†††††††††/4,7
(This is where Man's primitive self really plods to the fore. It recalls nothing so much as that desperate scrabble over the last bit of woolly mammoth marrow.)

Visit an exhibition of Japanese sword work — †††††††/15
(This should be taken as a metaphor. On Earth, there are any number of hobbyists — stamp-collectors, bird-song recorders, thimble painters, corn silk weavers, etc. — all of whom like nothing better than to show off their special interests to people who have nothing better to do before the pubs open. From the alien viewpoint, it is interesting to think that the same mind that created the neutron bomb also thought of putting ships in bottles.)

Go to a rock concert — †††/††††/7
(Millions are spent on rock concerts every year, and rock musicians are some of the most important and influential men on the planet. If you go to a concert you will find yourself packed in with thousands of other people, too far away to see the stage and unable to make out the lyrics [indeed, unable to make out anything but the drum and the comments of the chap behind you]. You will then wonder why rock musicians are some of the most

important and influential men on the planet. There's no reason for this, either.)

Places to Go

McDonald's — */**/***/****/†††††††††/5,6,7,12,13
There are several very attractive things about McDonald's. One is that you can find one almost anywhere in the world, and they are all exactly the same. Another is that, having been once, you will never understand why you go again. Yet another is that you will be half-way through your meal in the American Hamburger Restaurant in Pango Pango before you realize that you're not in McDonald's.

Major Cities — ****/*****/******/7,9,10,12,13,16
All major cities, from Paris to Moscow, from London to L.A., share certain qualities. High crime rates and pollution, dense populations, poor transport, the same chain restaurants, the same souvenir shops, statues of men on horseback in their parks, and the same musicals.

The Yorkshire Moors — */**/****/10,16
Forget the Sphinx, the Great Wall of China and the Taj Mahal. You haven't lived until you've seen the giant golf balls of the Yorkshire Moors, where you can see the acceptable face of nuclear threat, get a tan despite the weather and recharge your batteries at the same time.

A replica village — *******/********/1,5,9,12
For some reason, people think they want to know what it was like to live in the past. In reality, of course, no one is the least bit interested in living in a time when you had to carry cash, pee in a hole in the ground, or pick maggots out of your cheese. Thus Man invented the replica village. The replica village is like looking at photographs of daily life in 1772 while drinking Coca-Cola in a reproduction pewter mug.

The safari park — ***/†††/††††/9
The safari park allows you to sit in a bus on the grounds of what was once the stately home of one of the oldest families in Britain while watching a zebra stand under a tree in the rain. The safari park makes man feel a lot better about his treatment of other species, but it doesn't make them feel any better. The food is usually bad, the weather is usually worse, and the lions know bloody well that they're not on the savannah.

Las Vegas — ***/****/******/********/†††/††††††††/ 4,7,16
Paris is a major city. New York is a major city. Stockholm has its moments. But Las Vegas is not a major city. Las Vegas is the fantastical holographic projection of an inferior intelligence with adolescent hallucinations and advertizing dreams. Like the laser fields of Oj, it's worth seeing once, if only because if you hadn't seen it you would never believe it.

Last Chance, Oregon — **/********/1,3,4,5,12,16
The Bilvurions are giving a prize to anyone who can determine 'last chance' for what?

Flat 4, Humbleford Road, NW11 — ********/5,13
This is the residence of April Murgatroyd, a word processor operator by day and psychic by night and weekends. April's body is possessed not only by her, but by an Egyptian pharaoh, a Norse warrior, and a Native American medicine woman of the Crow tribe as well. For sixty pounds, April will read your cards, do your chart, and tell you whether or not you're likely to win the pools.

Arizona, USA — **/6
Many people believe that Arizona is the centre of ancient native magic and wisdom. Most of these people, interestingly enough, are white, not Native American. There are more people per mile in Arizona who are in touch with

187

John Lennon, Jim Morrison, or Elvis Presley than anywhere else in the world outside of Putney.

Texas — ********

An emergency room — ****/9,11
Nothing catches the full flavour, variety and timbre of human life like the emergency room of a large urban hospital. It has everything: drama, humour, joy and tears. Of course, you'd be ill-advised to visit in a real emergency, because it's unlikely that you'd be seen to in time.

A coffee shop — */3,12
In America, coffee shops are the only places you can go and be sure of finding a policeman. He will be eating a doughnut.

Eastern Europe — ***/****/*****/2,3,4,5,6,8,9,10,12
Eastern Europe was once extraordinarily beautiful and interesting, but the Russians took care of that pretty sharply. Now that Eastern Europe has been liberated, however, it is trying to encourage tourism again. Bring your own food and hold on to your Levis.

Red Neck Bar — */9,11
There are other places (e.g. parliament) where you can go to observe human male behaviour at its least inhibited, but the music and the food won't be as good.

Acknowledgements

The success of a project of this magnitude would never have been possible without the enthusiasm, encouragement, wit, wisdom, endurance, courage and tenacity of the countless individuals and organizations who, over the centuries, have explored and commented and reported on the Planet Earth — and so generously shared their findings with a curious if wary cosmos.

We would, therefore, like to extend our thanks to the following:

For Invaluable Factual Information and Topical Background

The Times
The New York Times
The Sunday Sport
The Sun
The National Inquirer
The TV Guide
Newsweek Magazine
Rolling Stone
Cosmopolitan
!Ola!
Elle
Der Spiegel
The Financial Times
News programmes and agencies, and radio and television stations throughout the world, with special thanks to TASS, UPI, the CBC, the BBC, and the NBC television network

For Invaluable Expert and Personal Advice

Penny Whistledown, teenager
Mrs Belinda Arbus, housewife
Richard Nixon, political theoretician
Sharon Campfield, shopper
Barbara Cartland, literary guru
Nancy Reagan, role model
Rocko Alleghany, small child and accomplished consumer
Margaret Thatcher, spiritual leader
Adam Spring, computer hacker and science fiction
   aficionado
Doug Espinoza, short-order cook and philosopher
Marcia Miller, exotic dancer
Janice Allman, animal lover
Boris Loftus, scientist and sperm donor
Emerald Browne, cheerleader
Omar Ubu, sportsman and business student
Max Landau, taxi-driver and observer of the human
   condition
James Special, McDonald's employee and observer of the
   human condition
Rufus and Enred May, fast food fans
Mary Louise Househop, true crime expert
Abe Spidle, motorcycle messenger
Mrs Arlene-Susanne Hepplemore, Christian
M.D. Lister, off-licence manager and human observer
Bernice Adie, driving instructor
Dr Stephanie Bickell-Hussey, psychologist and gardener
Miss Emma Woodruff, crossing guard
Sharon Hillslippe, wife and mother
Raymond C. Shakspear, city planner, computer enthusiast
   and amateur historian
Yolanda Herrera, real estate agent and UFO abductee
Burgess Endelheim, beautician and paranormal
Sky Rivers, cowboy and mystic
Tieng Lee Teoh, architect and surfer
B.B. Cooke, rock expert and historian

Abbey Skidmore, dental receptionist and channeller
Jackson 'Slash' Munroe, biker, musician, and observer of
the human condition
Hudson Swinhorne, solicitor and dabbler in human rights
Mr H.P. Schulman, atheist and salad chef
Jerome Mitchell, serious drinker and Trivial Pursuit
champion
Zach Sissel, unpublished writer
Mr and Mrs Beemish Fuller, Born Again Christians
Lt.Col.Aloysius P. Rumolsky, patriot and fighter
MTV
Spike, lead guitarist
All the folks at the Trout and Flag
The man on the bus with the live shrimp
Officer Petrolini, for his patience in explaining the law
Mrs Petrolini, for her patience in explaining the law
The shop assistant who elucidated free enterprise
The police forces of London, New York, Buenos Aires,
Manchester, Berlin, Barcelona, and, especially, Lost
Eagle, Wyoming
Pete Ford, football supporter and beer connoisseur
Leland Hopper, country singer
Jeff 'The Sticks' Codswill, rock drummer
Sunny Bartstein, model and expert on men
Dr Jane Ash, psychiatrist and expert on personal relations
Yeoman Michaels, poet and potter
Patty F, healthy liver and aerobics instructor
Mrs Alfred Patterson, knitter
Sumia, artist, mystic and tarot reader
Arturo Wallenstein, traveller and human observer
My mother, who loved to travel
My father, who preferred to stay home
And all the thousands of people, past and present, whose
knowledge helped us fail to understand

A Glossary of Useful Terms and Phrases

Almost home

'We're almost home'

This is a phrase that adult humans use to get their children to shut up during long journeys. What it means is that home is at least fifty miles away, but it's going to seem a lot farther if you don't stop whingeing.

All right

'It's all right.'
'You'll be all right.'
'Everything's going to be all right.'

All three of the above sentences seem to be suggesting that there is nothing wrong; that if there is something wrong, it isn't major; that everything will be fine at the end of the day.

In truth, however, what they are suggesting is that everything is awful; that you'll be lucky if you can ever rollerskate again; that things are probably a lot worse than you imagined.

For example: you are at Emily Poodle's house for tea. While you are sitting on her custom-made leather sofa, holding your tea in its Wedgwood cup in one hand and your open-face cucumber sandwich in the other, Emily is responding to your admiration of the carpet with a long story about her great-grandfather bringing it from Persia on the back of a camel. Just at that moment Emily's cat, Princess Margaret, comes into the room. She stands in the doorway for a moment, almost looking as though she's going to fall asleep where she stands. And then, faster than an electron, she shoots across the room, leaps into the air, bounces off your chest, and disappears over the sofa. You hadn't been expecting this. Your sandwich lands face down on the carpet, about a foot from where the tea cup smashes into 5,000 very tiny pieces and Earl Grey with lemon seeps across the floor. You say, 'Oh, my goodness, Emily, your carpet, I'm *so* terribly sorry!'

Emily says, 'Oh, please, don't worry. It's all right.'

Or, in other words, you've just ruined a priceless heirloom carpet and the only way you'll ever get into her house again is if you're working for the caterers.

Any minute now

Customer:	'I've been waiting in all morning for the man to come to connect the telephone. You said he'd be here between eight and noon, and it's already half-past one. When can I expect him?'
Service Representative:	'Any minute now.'

'Any minute now' is a polite way of saying either that he is never coming, or that he is at your house now, while you are around the corner phoning to see what's happened to him, and that he is slipping a note through the door that says Sorry We Missed You.

As soon as possible

This is one of those common Earth phrases that gives you more than one meaning to choose from.

If the phrase is used regarding you — as in, 'I want you to do that as soon as possible' — don't make the mistake of thinking it means at your earliest convenience. It means yesterday — as in, 'I wanted you to do it yesterday.'

The meaning changes slightly, however, if the person using it is speaking about themselves — as in 'Of course I'll do it as soon as possible.' In this case the phrase means 'when I get around to it' — as in, 'Of course I'll probably never do it.'

As you wish

Customer: 'But I don't want the green mini-skirt with the rhinestone hearts. I want the turquoise sheath with the six-inch slit.'
Salesperson: 'As you wish.'

You might think from the above that the salesperson was reaffirming the choice of the customer and showing approval, or at least acquiescence. But the salesperson is, in fact, doing no such thing. What s/he is doing is showing scorn, contempt, and the certain knowledge that when the customer goes out in the turquoise sheath everyone is going to be thinking, *I bet the salesperson tried to tell her she'd look like a blue banana that someone had started to peel in that dress.*

Back

Back in five minutes

You will often see signs like the above on shop doors. Back in five minutes. Back in ten minutes. Right back. Don't be deceived. The purpose of these signs is not, as you might think, to give you information (e.g. the owner of the shop will be back soon). The purpose of these signs is to let you know that though the shop isn't closed, it isn't open either.

'I'll be back' or 'I'll be right back'

Against everyone's better judgment, you have taken up with a human male. He is cute, he plays the banjo, and you find the way he sings 'Danny Boy' in the shower oddly endearing. One day, while you are repairing the stereo, he says, 'I'm just going out for a packet of gum, love. I'll be right back.' You are so sure that this means that he is going to be back as soon as he has gone down to the corner and bought his gum, that several hours pass while you fiddle with the tape deck before you realize that he hasn't come back yet. Chances are, of course, that you'll never see him again.

Be yourself

'Just be yourself and everyone will like you'

Only someone from Earth would tell you to be yourself, as though there's anyone else you could possibly be. But what seems at first glance a trite and meaningless phrase is, in fact, packed with significance. It says that both the speaker and the addressee know that it would be a lot better for everyone if the addressee were someone else, and that no one is ever going to like him no matter what he does unless he does actually become someone else.

Brilliant

Brilliant is an example of a word that is used so much that it is virtually without any meaning.

At best, it means 'not bad' — as in, 'What a brilliant idea!' or 'What a brilliant evening.'

At worst, it means god-awful — as in, 'Jeremy really is quite brilliant, you know.'

Communication

Of all the beings on the planet, humans are the only ones who speak.

A gorilla can give a cry of warning, but she can't explain if she's fleeing from a charging rhino or a man with a gun. A parrot can be taught to tell you that he's hungry, but he can't elaborate on what he wants to eat, whether his preference is for pesto or tomato sauce, whether grilled peppers give him heartburn or he already had broccoli for lunch. But a man can.

An infant can't tell you why he's crying, a chimpanzee can't tell you why she tipped her cereal bowl over your head, a dog can't explain his presence under the bed. But a human can.

Through words Man articulates his reality, gives shape to his fantasies, gives substance to his dreams. Through words he expresses his feelings and his thoughts, his nightmares and his fears. Language means that Man can understand both others and himself. Unlike every other creature on the planet, man doesn't have to rely on guesswork and instinct, on thuds and thumps and grunts and groans. With language Man can cross the chasm that separates self from self, can crawl on words from the burrow of his own brain and straight into another's heart.

Is it any wonder, then, that people are so big on communication? 'Talk to me,' they're always saying. 'Let's interface.' 'Let's discuss it.' 'Let's have a meaningful dialogue.'

Which makes it all the more strange that no one on this planet seems to understand anyone else. They talk and talk and talk, and then they go off and do exactly what they would have done if they hadn't spent twenty years in analysis and taken a course in language skills. You always know where you are with a barking dog, but never with a man.

Communism

In the Sternoid Galaxy, where it originated, Communism is a socio-economic theory based on communal ownership of the means of production and distribution. In Sternoid, Communism has produced flourishing societies of enviable social and economic equality, as well as astounding artistic achievements.

On the Earth there has been a certain amount of division regarding Communism. Half the planet thought it sounded like a good idea; and the other half thought that a society in which no one went hungry or homeless, and in which no one became wealthy at the expense of someone else, must be the work of the Devil.

Interestingly enough, in those countries where Communism was practised on Earth, it didn't produce the model societies of Sternoid with their intellectual and creative excitement and cheap rents. It produced repressive dictatorships and murals that might have been drawn by a Covian robot.

Consumer Society

The Communist leader Nikita Krushchev, in what was for him a moment of unusual levity, once promised the non-Communist countries of the West that Communism would take over the world. 'We will bury you,' Mr Kruschev told them. And then scuttled off to the back room to burst into giggles.

The people of the West didn't laugh. They decided to take this threat seriously. They began looking under their beds for Communists with shovels and buckets of dirt. They refused to watch the films of anyone who had ever said anything favourable about the unions. They suspected anyone built like a post-box of being a spy. So great was the fear and furore, in fact, that Jesus Christ, scheduled to make his second appearance on Earth in 1954 at the height of anti-Communist hysteria, cancelled his trip. 'It was bad enough being nailed to a cross,' Jesus said at the time. 'Can you imagine what they'd do to me now if I gave them the bit about the rich man getting into heaven and the eye of a needle? They'd electrocute me in Times Square.'

In reality, of course, the West never had anything to worry about, and they knew it. The Eastern bloc was going to bury them? What with? Potatoes? The West was sitting pretty. It had the ultimate secret weapon, the single most powerful thing ever invented on this planet of inventions. It had the consumer society.

As you might expect from its name, the consumer

society exists for the sole purpose of selling as many different things to the most people as often as possible. In the early days of the planet, it was thought that sentience was proof of existence. 'I think, therefore I am', was the popular phrase of the day. Now that has changed to, 'I shop, therefore I am'.

With the consumer society, Man has taken over the world, changing the global map into a profile of hamburger chains and cola bottling plants.

Countryside

'I love the countryside'

Never before in the history of the cosmos has anything been so idolized and sentimentalized, and at the same time so systematically destroyed — not to say razed to the ground — as the countryside of Earth (with the possible exception of Dresden).

Knowing how badly the countryside is treated (or mistreated), it may surprise you to hear so many people speak of it with so much longing and affection.

Fear not. They don't really mean it. What they mean is that they like to look at a few trees and a couple of stars now and then, but as soon as the mosquitos come out or they realize how far away they are from an all-night grocery, they start packing to go home.

Devil

'The devil made me do it'

Humans like to think of themselves as the nice guys of the cosmos. 'Hey,' they say, 'it's[37] not our fault. We're nice guys.'

---

[37] 'it's' here can stand for any number of things from the extinction of the eagle to the tower block.

On the other hand, of course, they have noticed that, considering what nice guys they all are, an awful lot happens on Earth that is not nice.

You can see the problem. It's your planet. You're the only species on it that can write a commercial or fire a gun. You make all the choices and decisions. You set the priorities and make the rules. You're a nice guy, but you've got millions of people hungry and homeless, burning rivers, solidifying oceans, evaporating species, and a hole in your atmosphere the size of Gealgoose. Who's to blame?

The Devil.

'You devil' or 'You little devil'

Aware of how much flak the devil takes every minute of the day, you might think that if someone were to say to you, 'You really are a devil, aren't you?', that s/he would be showing distrust and dislike. But *au contraire*. What s/he would be showing is a desire to turn off the lights and start an exchange of salivas.

Environmentalist

Earth is the only place in the cosmos where you would find a poodle in a tutu, a car horn that plays 'God Save the Queen', or butterless butter, cheeseless cheese, and saltless salt. It is also the only place where to be an 'environmentalist' is unusual. Everywhere else, to exist is to recognize that you are part of your environment, and responsible for it. But not here. Here, any untoward interest in keeping the trees standing, the birds flying, and the fish swimming is considered suspicious. At one time, if you evinced any interest in saving the whales people would have assumed that you were a Communist agitator. Now you're an environmentalist, which is slightly worse.

Rosemary: 'I hope you don't mind that I invited Marjory

to dinner on Friday, darling. I know she can be a bit of a bore if you get her talking about elephants and things like that, but she's actually quite sweet.'

Jonathan: 'Oh, my God, Marjory? Have you taken leave of your senses, darling? My boss is coming to this meal. What's he going to think when he finds himself sitting across from Marjory with her dolphin earrings and her Help the Earth Fight Back badge? [groans] This could cost me my promotion.'

Rosemary: 'Don't be silly, darling. I've told Marjory that she has to behave. "Adam V. Snaggle is Vice-President of a multinational conglomerate," I told her. "I don't want you offending him by bringing up the rain forests or that little oil spill off the coast of Alaska." And she promised she wouldn't say a word.'

Jonathan: [with a laugh like a verbal sneer] 'And you *believed* her? Darling, you know what these people are like. They have no sense of propriety or right. They have no sense of priorities. They're as bad as the Communists used to be, darling, they have no interest in profit.'

Rosemary: [patiently] 'Look, love, I know that Marjory doesn't use bleach or real detergents. And she does ride that horrible little pedal bike and refuse to kill flies, but she is an award-winning physicist, you know. I'm sure she can find something to talk about besides greenhouses.

Jonathan: [groaning] 'Wait a minute, darling. Wasn't it Marjory who dumped all that sludge in the office of the Minister of the Environment just because of his policy on nuclear wastes?'

Rosemary: 'She got a suspended sentence.'

Jonathan: [his voice becoming a little shrill] '*Suspended sentence*!?! Darling, you never told me that she was arrested. You've invited a known criminal to dinner with *my* boss? A man who has broken bread with prime ministers and kings? A man who plays golf with George Bush and Oliver North?'

Every effort is being made

'Every effort is being made to return your stolen possessions'
'Every effort is being made to bring the perpetrators to justice'
'Every effort is being made to find the party or parties responsible'

No effort whatsoever, in any shape or form, is being made.

Alternative phrase: 'We're doing everything we can.'

Freedom

J. Arthur Zap, in his pioneering study of human behaviour, *Progress: Yes or No?*, describes 'freedom' as the second most popular word on the planet, based on frequency of use.[38]

People are even bigger on freedom than they are on communication.

But as Zap explains in chapter two, 'freedom' is one of those tricky, subjective terms. One man's freedom, as they say, is another man's ball and chain.

In general, when you hear someone talking about 'freedom' (especially if he is linking it with 'liberty') you'd be well advised to head for the hills. Either he's going to shoot you, ask you to shoot someone else, or put you in jail.

---

[38] The most popular word is 'I'.

Headache

'Not tonight, dear, I have a headache'
'I'd love to come, Angie, but I have a headache'
'I was going to do it, but I had this killing headache'

A headache is a way of not doing something you never wanted or intended to do and gaining sympathy at the same time.

I

The most frequently used word on the planet.

As in:

'I never meant to hurt you', 'I didn't mean to do it', etc.

I certainly never meant to get caught.

'I'm on your side'

As long as you're on mine.

Liberty

Liberty is both the name of an exclusive British department store and of a human concept of personal freedom. In general, the former has been considerably more successful than the latter.

Male Bonding

Male bonding describes the special relationship that exists between men. This special relationship not only excludes women, it also explains why so many women find men impossible to understand or identify with.

Male bonding means that men, unlike women, do not base their friendships on an exchange of feelings, emotions, concerns and ideas. Instead they base them on

going to ball games, debating about whether or not Eric
Clapton or Jimi Hendrix is the better guitarist, drinking so
much alcohol that they pass out on the train-ride home
and wind up in Woking, and hanging out of car windows
going 'Woowoowoo, baby, hotchacha'.

Mother

Being a mother on this planet is like being both God and
the Devil: you are the most important and adored of
beings; and at the same time everything that goes wrong is
your fault.

Never Again

'I'll never buy another shirt'
'I'll never take another drink'
'I'll never go out with Derek again'
'I'll never eat another chocolate biscuit as long as I live'

Whenever you hear anyone make one of the above state-
ments you can be sure that they will.

Tea

'Have a cup of tea, you'll feel better'

In Great Britain tea is considered a general cure, a res-
torative, and a symbol of the traditions and beliefs on
which an empire was founded (class, colonialism, cheap
labour, and no more than fifteen minutes a day with the
children). In fact, tea is so important in British culture that
how to brew it, serve it and drink it is still a constant
source of argument and debate.

   This is an important concept to grasp, because many
aliens make the mistake of thinking that they are being
offered a drink when they're offered a cup of tea, and if
they don't feel thirsty they say, 'No thank you'. Never
refuse. They'll think you don't like them.

Afterword

'What a planet'
Kurt Vonnegut, Hocus Pocus

What a planet!

Index